W9-BSJ-079

PEARSON

TEXAS

ALGEBRA II

INTERACTIVE MATH JOURNAL
STUDENT COMPANION

PEARSON

Boston, Massachusetts • Chandler, Arizona • Glenview, Illinois • Hoboken, New Jersey

Cover Design: Tom White / 9 Surf Studio, Brian Reardon, Jamee Farinella.

Acknowledgements: **265** iStockphoto; **273** (TCR) iStockphoto, (CR) wingmar/iStockphoto; **339** Sly/Fotolia.

ISBN-13: 978-0-13-330073-4
ISBN-10:   0-13-330073-0

PEARSON

Contents

Using Your **Interactive Math Journal: Student Companion** with Success

The **Interactive Math Journal: Student Companion** is your in-class write-in worktext for *Pearson Texas Algebra II*. You will use your write-in worktext to work out solutions to problems presented and to check your understanding of concepts learned. Your **Interactive Math Journal: Student Companion** is available in print or as an ACTIVe-book, accessible through **PeasonTEXAS.com**.

STEP ONE

INTERACTIVE LEARNING

As your teacher projects the **Solve It** activity, you can collaborate with classmates to determine a solution to the problem posed. Work out your solution in your **Interactive Math Journal: Student Companion**. You can also take notes about the concepts presented. After a discussion of the solution, you'll be asked to complete the reflection question and think about the processes and strategies you used to solve the problem.

Look for the BouncePages icon on some **Solve Its**. Scan the page to access an animation for the problem.

Interactive Exploration

Vocabulary Online

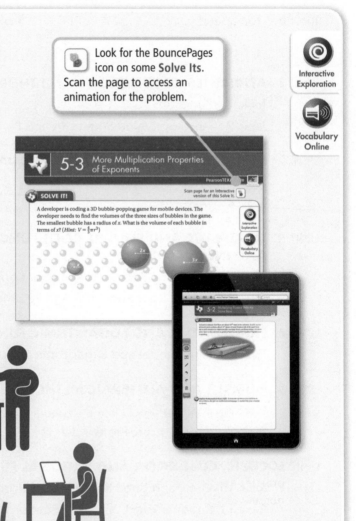

STEP TWO

GUIDED PROBLEM SOLVING

During the **Guided Problem Solving** part of the lesson, your teacher will guide you through the problems that introduce or reinforce important concepts and skills. After each problem, you work on the **Got It**, an exercise that applies the concepts and skills from the problem, to help solidify your understanding of these concepts.

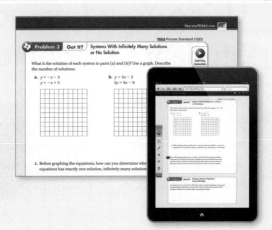

Learning Animation

STEP THREE

LESSON CHECK

At the end of each lesson is the **Lesson Check**. Each Lesson Check has two parts:

- **Do You Know How?** exercises help you gauge your procedural fluency.
- **Do You Understand?** exercises can give you a sense of how well you understand the lesson concepts.

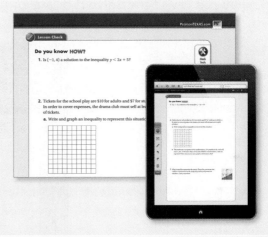

Math Tools

Online Practice

Virtual Nerd Tutorials

 TEXAS Test Practice

Your **Interactive Math Journal: Student Companion** also includes built-in **Texas Test Practice**. For each lesson, you'll find a page of practice exercises that are modeled after the assessment items you'll encounter on EOC Tests. Your teacher may assign these practice items to complete in class or for homework.

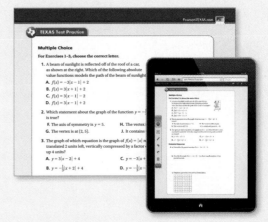

Using Your **Interactive Math Journal: Student Companion** ACTIVe-book

Your **Interactive Math Journal: Student Companion** is available as an ACTIVe-book, an interactive electronic workbook, that you can access on any device. In your ACTIVe-book, you can complete all of the exercises, and you can record all of your notes or reminders and access them any time and anywhere you can log in to **PearsonTEXAS.com**. You can also use the built-in communication tool to ask your teachers questions.

At the lesson level, you can access not just the pages in your **Interactive Math Journal: Student Companion,** but the digital assets as well. With the click of a tile, you can revisit the **Solve It** or any of the lesson problems.

Click on the tiles along the top row to work through the lesson.

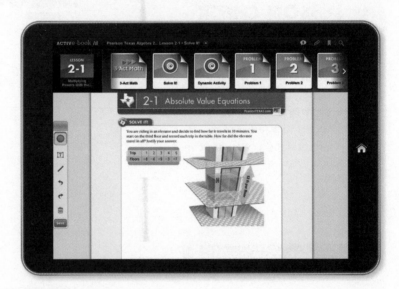

Use the different tools in the toolbar to record your answers and notes. Don't forget to click SAVE when you have finished.

Notice the ACTIVe-book toolbar on the left. You can place the toolbar where it is most convenient.

These features can help you stay organized and manage your work. You can see your assignments, chat with your teacher, bookmark a page, or access digital support tools.

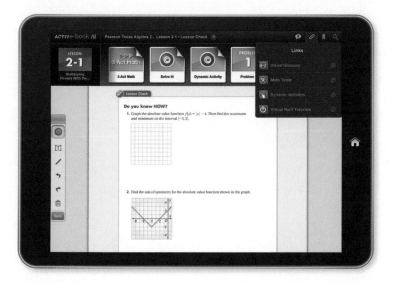

You have quick access to Math Tools, Visual Glossary, or even Online Homework.

The Super Stairs

Interactive Exploration

1. What is the first question that comes to mind after watching the video?

2. Write down the main question you will answer about what you saw in the video.

3. Make an initial conjecture that answers this main question.

4. Explain how you arrived at your conjecture.

5. Write a number that you know is too small.

6. Write a number that you know is too large.

7. What information will be useful to know to answer the main question? How can you get it? How will you use that information?

8. Use the math that you have learned in this topic to refine your conjecture.

9. Is your refined conjecture between the highs and lows you set up earlier?

10. Did your refined conjecture match the actual answer exactly? If not, what might explain the difference?

Topic 1 | 3-Act Math

T2

3-Act Math

The Draft Pick

Interactive Exploration

1. What is the first question that comes to mind after watching the video?

2. Write down the main question you will answer about what you saw in the video.

3. Make an initial conjecture that answers this main question.

4. Explain how you arrived at your conjecture.

5. What information will be useful to know to answer the main question? How can you get it? How will you use that information?

6. Use the math that you have learned in this topic to refine your conjecture.

3-Act Math

The Grand Coin Count

Interactive Exploration

1. What is the first question that comes to mind after watching the video?

2. Write down the main question you will answer about what you saw in the video.

3. Make an initial conjecture that answers this main question.

4. Explain how you arrived at your conjecture.

5. What information will be useful to know to answer the main question? How can you get it? How will you use that information?

6. Use the math that you have learned in this topic to refine your conjecture.

7. Did your refined conjecture match the actual answer exactly? If not, what might explain the difference?

The Big Burger

Interactive Exploration

1. What is the first question that comes to mind after watching the video?

2. Write down the main question you will answer about what you saw in the video.

3. Make an initial conjecture that answers this main question.

4. Explain how you arrived at your conjecture.

5. Write a number that you know is too small.

6. Write a number that you know is too large.

7. What information will be useful to know to answer the main question? How can you get it? How will you use that information?

8. Use the math that you have learned in this topic to refine your conjecture.

9. Is your refined conjecture between the highs and lows you set up earlier?

10. Did your refined conjecture match the actual answer exactly? If not, what might explain the difference?

3-Act Math

Piles of Tiles

Interactive Exploration

1. What is the first question that comes to mind after watching the video?

2. Write down the main question you will answer about what you saw in the video.

3. Make an initial conjecture that answers this main question.

4. Explain how you arrived at your conjecture.

5. Write a number that you know is too small.

6. Write a number that you know is too large.

7. What information will be useful to know to answer the main question? How can you get it? How will you use that information?

8. Use the math that you have learned in this topic to refine your conjecture.

9. Is your refined conjecture between the highs and lows you set up earlier?

10. Did your refined conjecture match the actual answer exactly? If not, what might explain the difference?

3-Act Math

Top Speed

Interactive Exploration

1. What is the first question that comes to mind after watching the video?

2. Write down the main question you will answer about what you saw in the video.

3. Make an initial conjecture that answers this main question.

4. Explain how you arrived at your conjecture.

5. Write a number that you know is too small.

6. Write a number that you know is too large.

7. What information will be useful to know to answer the main question? How can you get it? How will you use that information?

8. Use the math that you have learned in this topic to refine your conjecture.

9. Is your refined conjecture between the highs and lows you set up earlier?

10. Did your refined conjecture match the actual answer exactly? If not, what might explain the difference?

3-Act Math

The Crazy Conditioning

Interactive Exploration

1. What is the first question that comes to mind after watching the video?

2. Write down the main question you will answer about what you saw in the video.

3. Make an initial conjecture that answers this main question.

4. Explain how you arrived at your conjecture.

5. Write a number that you know is too small.

6. Write a number that you know is too large.

7. What information will be useful to know to answer the main question? How can you get it? How will you use that information?

8. Use the math that you have learned in this topic to refine your conjecture.

9. Is your refined conjecture between the highs and lows you set up earlier?

10. Did your refined conjecture match the actual answer exactly? If not, what might explain the difference?

3-Act Math

What Are the Rules?

Interactive
Exploration

1. What is the first question that comes to mind after watching the video?

2. Write down the main question you will answer about what you saw in the video.

3. Make an initial conjecture that answers this main question.

4. Explain how you arrived at your conjecture.

5. What information will be useful to know to answer the main question? How can you get it? How will you use that information?

6. Use the math that you have learned in this topic to refine your conjecture.

Topic 8 | 3-Act Math

T16

3-Act Math

The Snack Shack

Interactive
Exploration

1. What is the first question that comes to mind after watching the video?

2. Write down the main question you will answer about what you saw in the video.

3. Draw an initial conjecture that answers this main question.

4. Explain how you arrived at your conjecture.

5. What information will be useful to know to answer the main question? How can you get it? How will you use that information?

6. Use the math that you have learned in this topic to refine your conjecture.

7. Did your refined conjecture match the actual answer exactly? If not, what might explain the difference?

3-Act Math

The Big Blow Up

Interactive Exploration

1. What is the first question that comes to mind after watching the video?

2. Write down the main question you will answer about what you saw in the video.

3. Make an initial conjecture that answers this main question.

4. Explain how you arrived at your conjecture.

5. Write a number that you know is too small.

6. Write a number that you know is too large.

7. What information will be useful to know to answer the main question? How can you get it? How will you use that information?

8. Use the math that you have learned in this topic to refine your conjecture.

9. Is your refined conjecture between the highs and lows you set up earlier?

10. Did your refined conjecture match the actual answer exactly? If not, what might explain the difference?

3-Act Math

Real Cool Waters

Interactive Exploration

1. What is the first question that comes to mind after watching the video?

2. Write down the main question you will answer about what you saw in the video.

3. Make an initial conjecture that answers this main question.

4. Explain how you arrived at your conjecture.

5. Write a number that you know is too small.

6. Write a number that you know is too large.

7. What information will be useful to know to answer the main question? How can you get it? How will you use that information?

8. Use the math that you have learned in this topic to refine your conjecture.

9. Is your refined conjecture between the highs and lows you set up earlier?

10. Did your refined conjecture match the actual answer exactly? If not, what might explain the difference?

3-Act Math

The Express Lane

Interactive
Exploration

1. What is the first question that comes to mind after watching the video?

2. Write down the main question you will answer about what you saw in the video.

3. Make an initial conjecture that answers this main question.

4. Explain how you arrived at your conjecture.

5. What information will be useful to know to answer the main question? How can you get it? How will you use that information?

6. Use the math that you have learned in this topic to refine your conjecture.

7. Did your refined conjecture match the actual answer exactly? If not, what might explain the difference?

SOLVE IT!

The last digit in a 13-digit bar code is a check digit. Steps 1–3 show how the check digit checks the first 12 digits. Is it possible for 12 digits to generate two different check digits? Can two different sets of 12 digits have the same check digit? Explain.

Interactive Exploration

Vocabulary Online

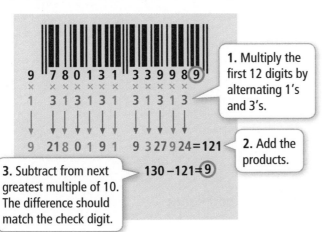

1. Multiply the first 12 digits by alternating 1's and 3's.

2. Add the products.

3. Subtract from next greatest multiple of 10. The difference should match the check digit.

Explain Mathematical Ideas (1)(G) A classmate questions your solution to the problem. Use precise mathematical language to explain why your solution is correct.

Problem 1 | **Got It?** | **Representing a Relation**

Learning Animation

The monthly average water temperature of the Gulf of Mexico in Key West, Florida varies during the year. In January, the average water temperature is 69°F, in February, 70°F, in March, 75°F, and in April, 78°F. How can you represent this relation in four different ways?

 Problem 2 | **Got It?** | **Finding Domain and Range**

Learning Animation

What are the domain and range of the relation?

$\{(-3, 14), (0, 7), (2, 0), (9, -18), (23, -99)\}$

 Problem 3 | **Got It?** | **Identifying Functions**

Learning Animation

Is the relation a function?

a. Domain   Range

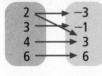

b. $\{(-7, 14), (9, -7), (14, 7), (7, 14)\}$

c. How does a mapping diagram of a relation that is not a function differ from a mapping diagram of a function?

Got It? **Using the Vertical-Line Test**

Use the vertical-line test. Which graph(s) represent functions?

a.   **b.**   **c.**

TEKS Process Standard (1)(E)

 Problem 5 **Got It?** **Using Function Notation**

For $f(x) = -4x + 1$, what is the output for the given input?

a. -2 **b.** 0 **c.** 5

ELPS Discuss with a classmate how your knowledge of *inputs* and *outputs* helps you use *function notation*. Solve the problem together.

Problem 6 **Got It?** **Using Interval and Set Notation**

The domain of $f(x)$ is $\{x \mid -2 < x \le 5\}$, and the range is $\{y \mid y \le 3\}$. Restate the domain and range of the function using interval notation.

Math Tools

Online Practice

Virtual Nerd Tutorials

Lesson Check

Do you know HOW?

1. Identify the domain and range of the relation $\{(3, -2), (4, 4), (0, -2), (4, 1), (3, 2)\}$. Then determine whether the relation is a function and explain your answer.

2. The relation $\{(2, -5), (8, -5), (3, 4), (a, 0)\}$ is not a function. What are the possible values of a?

3. A store sells a special olive oil in any amount from 2 to 6 ounces. The graph shows that the price of the oil is a function of the number of ounces. The store's owner decides to double the price of the oil. Write the domain and range of the new function using interval notation.

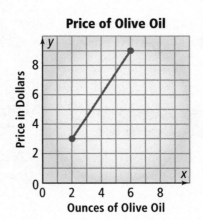

Price of Olive Oil

Do you UNDERSTAND?

Math
Tools

Online
Practice

Virtual Nerd
Tutorials

4. **Vocabulary** Does there exist a relation that is not a function? Does there exist a function that is not a relation? Explain.

5. **Explain Mathematical Ideas (1)(G)** Your friend writes, "In a function, every vertical line must intersect the graph in exactly one point." Do you agree? If so, explain why. If not, explain the error and rewrite the statement so that it is correct.

6. **Justify Mathematical Arguments (1)(G)** The domain of a relation is $\{-1, 2, 3, 6\}$. The range of the relation is $\{-2, -1, 2, 3, 4\}$. Is it possible for the relation to be a function? Justify your answer.

Multiple Choice

For Exercises 1–4, choose the correct letter.

1. The general admission rate to an amusement park is \$12. Each ride ticket costs \$2.75. Which of the following represents the cost for a day at the amusement park as a function of the number of ride tickets purchased?

   A. $C = 2.75t$

   B. $C = 12t + 2.75$

   C. $C = 12 + 2.75t$

   D. $C = 12t + 2.75t$

2. Which point could not be part of a function that includes $(3, -1)$, $(4, 2)$, $(5, 4)$, $(-2, 0)$, and $(8, -3)$?

   F. $(6, -7)$ **G.** $(3, -2)$ **H.** $(7, 4)$ **J.** $(2, 2)$

3. Which relations are functions?

   I.
   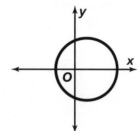

   III.
   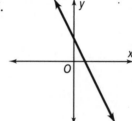

   II.
   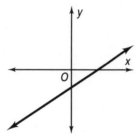

   IV.
   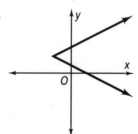

   A. II and III   **B.** I and II   **C.** III and IV   **D.** I and IV

4. The cost of renting a van at one rental service is represented by $C = 20 + 0.60m$, where C is the total cost and m is a whole number of miles. What is the range of the function for a trip greater than one mile?

   F. $\{C \mid C > 20\}$ **G.** $\{C \mid C \geq 20\}$ **H.** $\{C \mid C > 20.60\}$ **J.** $\{C \mid C \geq 20.60\}$

Short Response

5. A phone store employee earns a salary of \$450 per week plus 10% commission on her weekly sales.

   a. What function rule models the employee's weekly earnings?

   b. If the employee earned \$570 in a week, what was the amount of her sales for that week?

SOLVE IT!

Each graph represents a function. Describe several qualities of each graph. How are the qualities the same? How are they different?

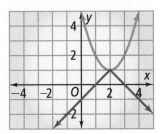

Interactive Exploration

Vocabulary Online

 Connect Mathematical Ideas (1)(F) What prior knowledge did you draw on to solve the problem?

Problem 1 | **Got It?** | **Graphing and Analyzing a Function**

Learning
Animation

Graph the function $f(x) = 3 - x$. Then find the domain, range, and intercepts of the function. What is the minimum and maximum value of $f(x)$ on the interval $[-7, -1]$?

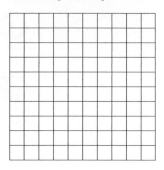

ELPS Draw a four-corner graphic organizer titled "Families of Functions." Copy each of the parent graph equations shown on the board in one of the corners. Graph the equations and choose the correct family label: *linear, cubic, quadratic,* and *square root.* Read each part of the model aloud with a classmate, then choose the correct category for the Got It. As you read more about functions in this topic, refer to your chart. Add examples and information when possible.

Problem 2 **Got It?** Analyzing Key Attributes of $f(x) = x^3$

Learning
Animation

Your classmate graphs the function $g(x) = 2x^3$. He says that compared to its parent function, the y-intercept of $g(x)$ shifts up 2 units to $(0, 2)$. Do you agree? Explain.

Problem 3 **Got It?** Analyzing Key Attributes of $f(x) = \frac{1}{x}$

Learning
Animation

Your friend says the graph of $y = \frac{1}{x}$ is symmetric over both the x-axis and the y-axis. Is your friend correct? Explain why or why not.

Lesson 1-2 | Attributes of Functions

9

Lesson Check

Do you know HOW?

1. Graph the function $f(x) = x^3 - 1$. State the x-intercept and y-intercept, and give the domain and range in interval notation.

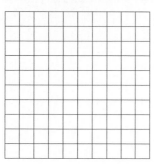

Math Tools

Online Practice

Virtual Nerd Tutorials

2. The graph of $g(x) = ax + b$ has an x-intercept of $(2, 0)$ and a y-intercept of $(0, 6)$. What are the values of a and b?

3. Several friends contribute equally to buy a birthday gift that costs $24. The function $f(x) = \frac{24}{x}$ represents the amount of money each of x friends must contribute. Graph the function and explain what the horizontal asymptote represents in this context.

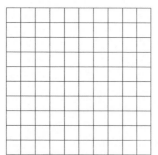

Lesson 1-2 | Attributes of Functions

Do you UNDERSTAND?

Math Tools

Online Practice

Virtual Nerd Tutorials

4. Vocabulary Explain why the word *parent* makes sense in the term *parent function*.

5. Explain Mathematical Ideas (1)(G) Do the domain and range of the function $f(x) = x^3 + k$ depend on the value of k? Explain why or why not.

6. Use Representations to Communicate Mathematical Ideas (1)(E) Consider the linear function $f(x) = mx + b$, where $m \neq 0$, on the interval $[3, 7]$. Explain why the maximum value of the function over this interval must occur at one of the endpoints of the interval.

TEXAS Test Practice

Multiple Choice

For Exercises 1–5, choose the correct letter.

1. The function $f(m) = 400 - 50m$ models the height f of a hot-air balloon, in feet, as it descends, where m is the number of minutes that have elapsed since the start of the descent. In this situation, what are the domain and range for this function?

   A. domain: $[0, \infty)$
   range: $[400, \infty)$

   B. domain: $[0, 8]$
   range: $[0, 400]$

   C. domain: $[0, \infty)$
   range: $[0, 400]$

   D. domain: $[0, 8]$
   range: $[400, \infty)$

2. Consider the functions $f(x) = x^2$ and $g(x) = x^3$. Which statement about the functions is not true?

   F. The functions have the same x-intercept.

   G. The functions have the same y-intercept.

   H. The functions have the same domain.

   J. The functions have the same range.

3. The function $h(x) = 2x + c$ has a maximum value of 6 on the interval $[0, 1]$. What is the value of c?

   A. 2   **B.** 3   **C.** 4   **D.** 6

4. Marcus uses software to graph $f(x) = 3x + 2$. Then he changes the function to $f(x) = 3x - 2$ and uses the software to graph the new function. Which of the following attributes of the function changes?

   F. domain   **H.** range

   G. y-intercept   **J.** asymptote

5. For which function are the x-intercept and the y-intercept the same point?

   A. $f(x) = x^3$ **B.** $f(x) = \frac{1}{x}$ **C.** $f(x) = x - 1$ **D.** $f(x) = 1$

Extended Response

6. A rectangular sticker has an area of 10 square centimeters. The function $f(x) = \frac{10}{x}$ models the width f of the sticker, in centimeters, when the length is x centimeters. Graph the function and identify the horizontal asymptote. What does the asymptote represent in this context?

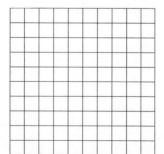

Lesson 1-2 | Attributes of Functions

SOLVE IT!

You want to buy a sofa that has already been marked down by $100. The furniture store may add the 5% sales tax before applying the additional discount, or it may add the sales tax after applying the additional discount. Which way is better for you, the customer? How much better?

Interactive Exploration

Vocabulary Online

Clearance sale
Take $50 off

 Explain Mathematical Ideas (1)(G) A classmate questions your solution to the problem. Use precise mathematical language to explain why your solution is correct.

TEKS Process Standard (1)(E)

 Problem 1 | **Got It?** | **Adding and Subtracting Functions**

Learning
Animation

Let $f(x) = 2x^2 + 8$ and $g(x) = x - 3$. What are $f + g$ and $f - g$? What are their domains?

 Problem 2 | **Got It?** | **Multiplying and Dividing Functions**

Learning
Animation

Let $f(x) = 3x^2 - 11x - 4$ and $g(x) = 3x + 1$. What are $f \cdot g$ and $\frac{f}{g}$ and their domains?

Problem 3 | **Got It?** | **Composing Functions**

Let $f(x) = x - 5$ and $g(x) = x^2$. What is $(f \circ g)(-3)$?

Learning Animation

ELPS Explain *function composition* in your own words using the terms *input, output,* and *expression*. Ask your partner questions about function composition such as: Will you explain what ___ means?

 Problem 4 | **Got It?** | **Using Composite Functions**

A store is offering a 15% discount on all items. Also, employees get a 20% employee discount. Write composite functions

Learning Animation

a. to model taking the 15% discount and then the 20% discount.

b. to model taking the 20% discount and then the 15% discount.

c. If you were an employee, which discount would you take first? Why?

Lesson Check

Do you know HOW?

1. Let $f(x) = 3x - 2$ and $g(x) = 4x + 1$. Find $(f - g)(x)$ and $(f \circ g)(x)$.

2. Use the tables to find $(f \circ g)(2)$ and $(g \circ f)(4)$.

x	1	2	3	4
f(x)	0	−5	−2	1

x	1	2	3	4
g(x)	−5	3	0	2

3. The graphs of three functions are shown. What are $(g \circ f)(-1)$ and $(h \circ g)(1)$?

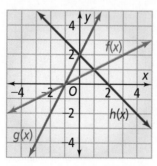

Lesson Check

Do you UNDERSTAND?

Math Tools

Online Practice

Virtual Nerd Tutorials

4. **Vocabulary** Explain what a composite function has in common with a composite figure and a composite number.

5. **Evaluate Reasonableness (1)(B)** Your friend used some simple functions and found that $(f \circ g)(x) = (g \circ f)(x)$, and concluded that function composition is commutative. Is your friend's conclusion reasonable? If so, why? If not, give an example to show that your friend is mistaken.

6. **Analyze Mathematical Relationships (1)(F)** Find two functions f and g such that $f(g(x)) = x$ for all real numbers x.

TEXAS Test Practice

Multiple Choice

For Exercises 1–5, choose the correct letter.

1. A store is offering a 20% discount off one item. You also have a coupon for $5 off one item. Which composite function represents the final price if the coupon is applied before the discount?

   A. $(g \circ f)(x) = .20x - 1$ **C.** $(g \circ f)(x) = .80x - 4$

   B. $(g \circ f)(x) = .20x - 5$ **D.** $(g \circ f)(x) = .80x - 5$

2. Let $f(x) = 3x$ and $g(x) = x^2 + 1$. What is $(f \cdot g)(x)$?

   F. $9x^2 + 3x$ **H.** $3x^3 + 3x$

   G. $9x^2 + 1$ **J.** $3x^3 + 1$

3. Let $f(x) = -2x + 5$ and $g(x) = x^3$. What is $(g - f)(x)$?

   A. $x^3 - 2x + 5$ **C.** $-x^3 - 2x + 5$

   B. $x^3 + 2x - 5$ **D.** $-x^3 + 2x - 5$

4. Let $f(x) = x + 5$ and $g(x) = 2x + 1$. Which of the following is not true?

   F. The domain of f is all real numbers except $x \neq -5$.

   G. The domain of $f + g$ is all real numbers.

   H. The domain of $\frac{g}{f}$ is all real numbers except $x \neq -5$.

   J. The domain of $f \circ g$ is all real numbers.

5. Let $f(x) = \frac{1}{x}$ and $g(x) = x^2 - 2$. What is $(f \circ g)(-3)$?

   A. $\frac{17}{9}$ **B.** $\frac{1}{7}$ **C.** $-\frac{17}{9}$ **D.** $-\frac{7}{3}$

Short Response

6. Suppose the function $f(x) = 0.035x$ represents the number of U.S. dollars equivalent to x Russian rubles, and the function $g(x) = 90x$ represents the number of Japanese yen equivalent to x U.S. dollars. Write a composite function that represents the number of Japanese yen equivalent to x Russian rubles. Show your work.

Scan page for an interactive
version of this Solve It.

What is wrong with the headline? Why? What headline would you write? How
much of an increase should the Mayor receive to make the existing headline true?

Interactive
Exploration

Vocabulary
Online

> The Community Times   Thursday Morning Edition
>
> **Mayor's Salary Restored**
> At last night's meeting, the town
> council approved a 20% increase in the
> mayor's salary. This follows last year's
> 20% decrease. The Mayor's comment was

Connect Mathematical Ideas (1)(F) How does this problem relate to a problem
you have seen before?

Problem 1 | **Got It?** | Finding the Inverse of a Relation

Learning
Animation

a. What are the graphs of *t* and its inverse?

Relation t

x	0	1	2	3
y	−5	−4	−3	−3

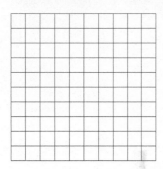

b. Is *t* a function? Is the inverse of *t* a function? Explain.

ELPS Discuss the terms *inverse* and *inverse function* with a classmate. Listen to your classmate explain the steps for solving part (b). Repeat what you hear with statements like: What I heard you say was ___.

 Problem 2 | **Got It?** | Finding an Equation for the Inverse

Learning
Animation

What is the inverse of $y = x^3 + 8$?

TEKS Process Standard (1)(F)

 Problem 3 **Got It?** Graphing a Function and Its Inverse

a. Graph $f(x) = 2x + 8$ and its inverse, $f^{-1}(x) = 0.5x - 4$.

Learning Animation

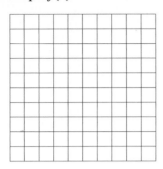

b. Is $f(x)$ one-to-one? Explain your answer.

c. Analyze the relationship between $f(x)$ and $f^{-1}(x)$. What restrictions on the domain of $f(x)$ make $f^{-1}(x)$ a function?

Lesson 1-4 | Inverse Functions

21

TEKS Process Standard (1)(A)

 Problem 4 | **Got It?** | Finding the Inverse When the Domain and Range Have Restrictions

Learning Animation

Let $g(x) = \sqrt{2x - 4}$.

a. What are the domain and range of g?

b. What is the inverse of g?

c. What are the domain and range of g^{-1}?

d. Is g^{-1} a function? Explain.

Lesson 1-4 | Inverse Functions

22

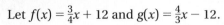

Learning Animation

Let $f(x) = \frac{3}{4}x + 12$ and $g(x) = \frac{4}{3}x - 12$.

a. What is $(f \circ g)(x)$?

b. What is $(g \circ f)(x)$?

c. Are f and g inverse functions? Explain.

Lesson Check

Do you know HOW?

Math Tools

Online Practice

Virtual Nerd Tutorials

1. Consider the function $f(x) = 2x - 1$. What is f^{-1}? Graph f and f^{-1} and describe how the graphs are related.

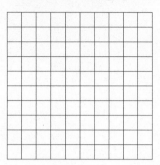

2. Given the function $g(x) = \frac{1}{x + 4}$, what is $g^{-1}(x)$? What is the domain of $g^{-1}(x)$?

3. A tank has 55 gallons of water in it. The water drains from the tank at the rate of 3 gallons per minute. The function $f(x)$ models the number of gallons of water in the tank after x minutes. Find $f^{-1}(15)$ and explain what it represents.

Lesson Check

Do you UNDERSTAND?

Math Tools

Online Practice

Virtual Nerd Tutorials

4. **Vocabulary** Does every function have an inverse which is a function? Does every relation have an inverse which is a relation? Explain.

5. **Explain Mathematical Ideas (1)(G)** A friend states that it is possible for a function to be its own inverse. Do you agree or disagree? If you agree, give an example of such a function and tell why the function is its own inverse. If you disagree, explain why.

6. **Create Representations to Communicate Mathematical Ideas (1)(E)** If a relation is not a function, is it possible for its inverse to be a function? Provide a mapping diagram, an equation, and a graph to support your answer.

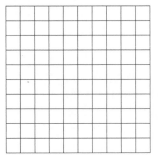

TEXAS Test Practice

Multiple Choice

For Exercises 1–4, choose the correct letter.

1. According to a cookbook, the time m in minutes to cook an 8 to 12 pound turkey is given by the function $m(x) = 20x + 20$, where x is the weight of the turkey in pounds. What is the domain of $m^{-1}(x)$ in this situation?

   A. $[8, 12]$ **C.** $[180, \infty)$

   B. $[180, 260]$ **D.** $[0, 260]$

2. Given that $f(7) = -2$ and $f^{-1}(4) = -2$, which of the following statements must be true?

   F. $f(4) = -2$ **H.** $f^{-1}(7) = -2$

   G. $f(-2) = 7$ **J.** $f^{-1}(-2) = 7$

3. The graph of the function g is shown at the right. Which of the following is a true statement about g^{-1}?

   A. $g^{-1}(-2) = 0$

   B. The domain of g^{-1} is $[-2, 4]$.

   C. The range of g^{-1} is $[-2, 4]$.

   D. The graph of g^{-1} lies entirely below the x-axis.

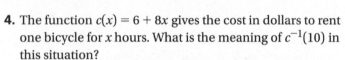

4. The function $c(x) = 6 + 8x$ gives the cost in dollars to rent one bicycle for x hours. What is the meaning of $c^{-1}(10)$ in this situation?

   F. the cost of renting a bicycle for 10 hours

   G. the cost of renting 10 bicycles

   H. the number of hours you can rent a bicycle for $10

   J. the number of bicycles you can rent for $10

Extended Response

5. The function $f(x) = 2x + 4$ gives the total cost f in dollars, including shipping, when you buy x ounces of tea at an online store. However, the function only applies to amounts of tea from 1 to 4 ounces.

   a. Write a rule for f^{-1} and graph f^{-1}.

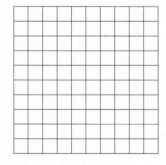

   b. Give the domain and range of f^{-1} in this situation.

Scan page for an interactive
version of this Solve It.

Two local car-sharing companies each charge a monthly membership fee in addition to an hourly rental rate. In one month, can a customer at Company A and a customer at Company B pay the same total cost? If so, when? How do you know?

Interactive Exploration

Vocabulary Online

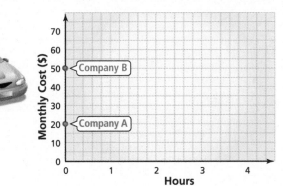

Use Multiple Representations to Communicate Mathematical Ideas (1)(D)
What is another representation you could use to solve the problem? Explain why the representation would be useful.

Problem 1 | **Got It?** | **Using a Graph or Table to Solve a System**

What is the solution of the system? $\begin{cases} x - 2y = 4 \\ 3x + y = 5 \end{cases}$

Learning Animation

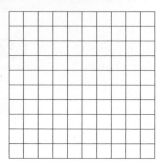

 Problem 2 | **Got It?** | **Using a Table to Solve a Problem**

A spiny dogfish shark has a birth length of 22 cm and a growth rate of 1.5 cm/yr. A Greenland shark has a birth length of 37 cm and a growth rate of 0.75 cm/yr.

 Learning Animation

a. If the growth rates continue, how long will each shark be when it is 25 years old?

b. Explain why growth rates for these sharks may not continue indefinitely.

ELPS Discuss part (b) with a classmate. How would you rephrase the question? What do you know about sharks that helps you answer this question?

Problem 3 **Got It?** **Using Linear Regression**

Learning Animation

The table shows the populations of the San Diego and Detroit metropolitan regions. When were the populations of these regions equal? What was that population?

Populations of San Diego and Detroit Metropolitan Regions (1950–2000)

	1950	1960	1970	1980	1990	2000
San Diego	334,387	573,224	696,769	875,538	1,110,549	1,223,400
Detroit	1,849,568	1,670,144	1,511,482	1,203,339	1,027,974	951,270

SOURCE: U.S. Census Bureau

 Problem 4 **Got It?** **Classifying a System Without Graphing**

Learning Animation

Without graphing, is each system *independent*, *dependent*, or *inconsistent*?

a. $\begin{cases} -3x + y = 4 \\ x - \frac{1}{3}y = 1 \end{cases}$

b. $\begin{cases} 2x + 3y = 1 \\ 4x + y = -3 \end{cases}$

c. $\begin{cases} y = 2x - 3 \\ 6x - 3y = 9 \end{cases}$

Lesson Check

Do you know HOW?

1. Solve the system of linear equations by graphing. Check your solution.
$$\begin{cases} y = x - 1 \\ y = -x + 3 \end{cases}$$

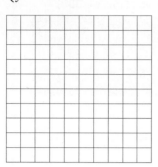

Math Tools

Online Practice

Virtual Nerd Tutorials

2. Without graphing, determine whether the system of equations is *inconsistent*, *dependent*, or *independent*.
$$\begin{cases} 3x + 4y = 40 \\ x - 2y = 8 \end{cases}$$

3. A monthly pass at a dance studio costs $30. With the pass, each dance session costs $2, and without the pass, each session costs $8. How many classes per month must your friend take for the monthly cost to be the same with or without a pass? Solve using a table.

Lesson Check

Do you UNDERSTAND?

Math Tools

Online Practice

Virtual Nerd Tutorials

4. **Vocabulary** Explain whether or not it is possible for a system of equations to be both independent and inconsistent.

5. **Explain Mathematical Ideas (1)(G)** Given one linear equation, explain how to write a second linear equation that results in a system with no solution.

6. **Analyze Mathematical Relationships (1)(F)** In a particular system of linear equations, the slope of one of the lines is the negative reciprocal of the slope of the other line. How many solutions does this system have? Is this system consistent? Is it dependent?

TEXAS Test Practice

Multiple Choice

For Exercises 1–4, choose the correct letter.

1. You and your friend are both knitting scarves for charity. You knit 8 rows each minute and have already knitted 10 rows. Your friend knits 5 rows each minute and has already knitted 19 rows. After how many minutes will you both have knitted the same number of rows?

   A. 2.6 minutes   **B.** 3 minutes   **C.** 9.7 minutes   **D.** 34 minutes

2. Which ordered pair of numbers is the solution of the system? $\begin{cases} 2x + 3y = 12 \\ 2x - y = 4 \end{cases}$

   F. $(2, 3)$ **G.** $(3, 2)$ **H.** $(1, -2)$ **J.** $(-3, 6)$

3. Which of the following graphs shows the solution of the system?
   $\begin{cases} x + y = -4 \\ 2x - 2y = -8 \end{cases}$

   A. 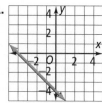   **C.**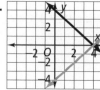

   B. 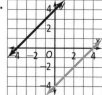   **D.**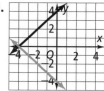

4. For which of the following systems is there no point (x, y) which satisfies the system?

   F. $\begin{cases} x + y = 4 \\ x - y = 3 \end{cases}$ **H.** $\begin{cases} 6x + 3y = 12 \\ 2y = -4x + 4 \end{cases}$

   G. $\begin{cases} 2y - x = 5 \\ 4y = 2x + 10 \end{cases}$ **J.** $\begin{cases} -3x + y = 4 \\ 2y = -6x + 8 \end{cases}$

Short Response

5. The sides of an angle are two lines whose equations are $4x + y = 12$ and $y = 2x$. An angle has its vertex at the point where the lines meet.
   Use a graph to determine the coordinates of the vertex. What are the coordinates of the vertex?

SOLVE IT!

What whole-dollar amount of per-day sales would make it more worthwhile to work at Store B? Justify your reasoning.

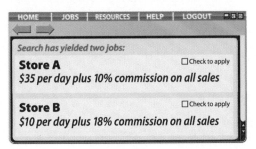

HOME | JOBS | RESOURCES | HELP | LOGOUT

Search has yielded two jobs:

Store A ☐ Check to apply
$35 per day plus 10% commission on all sales

Store B ☐ Check to apply
$10 per day plus 18% commission on all sales

Interactive Exploration

Vocabulary Online

★ **Create Representations to Communicate Mathematical Ideas (1)(E)**
Describe how the representation you made successfully organizes and communicates your solution to the problem.

Problem 1 **Got It?** **Solving by Substitution**

What is the solution of the system of equations? $\begin{cases} x + 3y = 5 \\ -2x - 4y = -5 \end{cases}$

Learning Animation

TEKS Process Standard (1)(A)

 Problem 2 **Got It?** **Using Substitution to Solve a Problem**

An online music company offers 15 downloads for $19.75 and 40 downloads for $43.50. Each price includes the same one-time registration fee. What is the cost of each download and the registration fee?

Learning Animation

 Problem 3 **Got It?** **Solving by Elimination**

What is the solution of the system of equations? $\begin{cases} -2x + 8y = -8 \\ 5x - 8y = 20 \end{cases}$

Learning Animation

Lesson 3-2 | Solving Systems Algebraically

Problem 4 | **Got It?** | Solving an Equivalent System

a. What is the solution of this system of equations? $\begin{cases} 3x + 7y = 15 \\ 5x + 2y = -4 \end{cases}$

Learning Animation

b. In Problem 4, you found that $y = 2$. Substitute this value into $3x + 5y = -5$ instead of $2x + 7y = 4$. Do you still get the same value for x? Explain why.

TEKS Process Standard (1)(G)

 Problem 5 | **Got It?** | Solving Systems Without Unique Solutions

What are the solutions of the following systems? Explain.

a. $\begin{cases} -x + y = -2 \\ 2x - 2y = 0 \end{cases}$

Learning Animation

b. $\begin{cases} 4x + y = 6 \\ 12x + 3y = 18 \end{cases}$

ELPS Discuss the problem with a classmate. To use elimination, what must you do to the system in part (a)? What about part (b)? Solve these systems by sharing information. Interpret your solutions graphically. What does the graph of a system with no solutions look like? Infinite solutions? One solution?

Lesson 3-2 | Solving Systems Algebraically

67

Lesson Check

Do you know HOW?

1. Use substitution to find the solution of this system of linear equations.

$$\begin{cases} x - 2y = -6 \\ 2x + 3y = 2 \end{cases}$$

Math
Tools

Online
Practice

Virtual Nerd
Tutorials

2. A local gym has a membership fee of $200 in addition to a $40 monthly fee. A sports club has a membership fee of $350 but has a monthly fee of only $30. After how many months will the sports club be a better deal than the local gym?

3. When $h \neq 0$, what is the solution of the system $2hx + 6y = 8$ and $hx - 6y = -12$?

Lesson Check

Math Tools

Online Practice

Virtual Nerd Tutorials

Do you UNDERSTAND?

4. Vocabulary Give an example of two equivalent systems.

5. Analyze Mathematical Relationships (1)(F) Explain how the substitution method of solving a system of equations differs from the elimination method.

6. Select Techniques to Solve Problems (1)(C) A café sells a regular cup of coffee for $1 and a large cup for $1.50. Melissa and her friends buy 5 cups of coffee and spend a total of $6. Write and solve a system of equations to find the number of large cups of coffee they bought. Describe which method you used and why.

TEXAS Test Practice

Multiple Choice

For Exercises 1–4, choose the correct letter.

1. At a bookstore, used hardcover books sell for $8 each, and used softcover books sell for $2 each. You purchase 36 used books and spend $144. How many softcover books do you buy?

   A. 9   **B.** 12   **C.** 18   **D.** 24

Use the system of equations for Exercises 2 and 3. $\begin{cases} 4x - 10y = -3 \\ 12x + 5y = 12 \end{cases}$

2. What is the value of x in the solution?

   F. $-\frac{9}{7}$ **G.** $-\frac{15}{28}$ **H.** $\frac{3}{5}$ **J.** $\frac{3}{4}$

3. What is the value of y in the solution?

   A. $\frac{3}{35}$ **B.** $\frac{3}{5}$ **C.** $\frac{3}{4}$ **D.** $\frac{24}{35}$

4. A system of equations is given by $\begin{cases} ax + by = c \\ x = 3 \end{cases}$, for constants a, b, and c, with $b \neq 0$. How many solutions does this system have?

   F. zero   **G.** one   **H.** two   **J.** infinitely many

Extended Response

5. A local cell phone company offers two different calling plans. In the first plan, you pay a monthly fee of $30 and $.35 per minute. In the second plan, you pay a monthly fee of $99 and $.05 per minute.

   a. Write a system of equations showing the two calling plans.

   b. When is it better to use the first calling plan?

   c. When is it better to use the second calling plan?

   d. How much does it cost when the calling plans are equal?

Lesson 3-2 | Solving Systems Algebraically

SOLVE IT!

You want a car that costs less than $20,000 after 5% sales tax is added. You want fuel costs under $1200 for the 10,000 city miles you expect to drive next year. You estimate that the cost of gas will average $4 per gallon. Which car meets your conditions? Explain.

Interactive Exploration

Vocabulary Online

Model A	Model B	Model C	Model D	Model E	Model F	Model G	Model H
$19,500	$19,000	$19,999	$19,250	$22,711	$18,995	$16,435	$18,434
City MPG 39	City MPG 29	City MPG 35	City MPG 32	City MPG 27	City MPG 24	City MPG 37	City MPG 31

 Use a Problem-Solving Model (1)(B) Evaluate your problem-solving model. Which parts were helpful? Which would you want to revise? Explain.

Problem 1 Got It? Solving a System by Using a Table

Learning
Animation

Assume that x and y are whole numbers. What is the solution of the system of inequalities?

$$\begin{cases} x + y > 4 \\ 3x + 7y \le 21 \end{cases}$$

 Problem 2 Got It? Solving a System by Graphing

What is the solution of the system of inequalities? $\begin{cases} x + 2y \le 4 \\ y \ge -x - 1 \end{cases}$

Learning
Animation

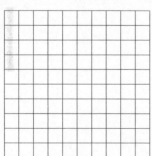

ELPS Discuss the steps for solving with a classmate. How is the solution for a system of inequalities represented on a graph? How can you be sure you have the correct answer?

Problem 3 **Got It?** Using a System of Inequalities

TEKS Process Standard (1)(A)

A pizza parlor charges $1 for each vegetable topping and $2 for each meat topping. You want at least five toppings on your pizza. You have $10 to spend on toppings. How many of each type of topping can you get on your pizza?

Learning Animation

Lesson Check

Do you know HOW?

1. Solve the system of inequalities by graphing. $\begin{cases} x + y \geq 2 \\ 2x + y \leq 5 \end{cases}$

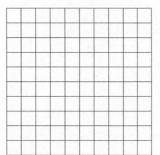

 Math Tools

 Online Practice

Virtual Nerd Tutorials

2. Solve this system of inequalities by graphing. $\begin{cases} y > -4x + 2 \\ y < 5 \\ y + 1 \geq \frac{1}{4}x \end{cases}$

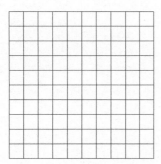

3. Write a system of inequalities for the shaded region in the diagram.

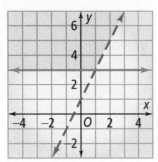

Lesson 3-3 | Systems of Inequalities

74

Lesson Check

Do you UNDERSTAND?

Math
Tools

Online
Practice

Virtual Nerd
Tutorials

4. **Vocabulary** Is the solution of a system of linear inequalities the *union* or *intersection* of the solutions of the two inequalities? Justify your answer.

5. **Analyze Mathematical Relationships (1)(F)** Explain how the graphical solution of a system of inequalities is different from the graphical solution of a system of equations.

6. **Justify Mathematical Arguments (1)(G)** Your classmate graphs the system of inequalities below. Is the graph correct? Justify your answer.

$$\begin{cases} y < \frac{1}{2}x - 1 \\ y > -3x + 3 \end{cases}$$

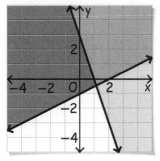

 **TEXAS Test Practice**

Multiple Choice

For Exercises 1–4, choose the correct letter.

1. You are having a bake sale for charity and hope to raise at least $50. You will sell pies for $7 and cookies for $2. You have only enough pie crust dough to make 5 pies at most. Which of the following systems of inequalities models the number of pies and cookies you must sell to reach your fundraising goal?

   A. $\begin{cases} 7x + 2y \le 50 \\ 7x \le 5 \end{cases}$ **C.** $\begin{cases} 7x - 2y \le 50 \\ 35x \le 50 \end{cases}$

   B. $\begin{cases} 7x + 2y \ge 50 \\ x \le 5 \end{cases}$ **D.** $\begin{cases} 7x + 2y \ge 50 \\ y \le 5 \end{cases}$

2. Which of the following graphs shows the solution of the system of inequalities? $\begin{cases} y \ge -2x + 2 \\ y \le |3x| \end{cases}$

   F. 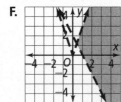   **G.** 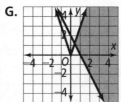   **H.** 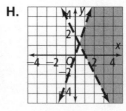   **J.**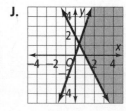

3. Which point lies in the solution set for the system? $\begin{cases} y > x + 1 \\ x \ge a \end{cases}$

   A. $(0, 0)$ **B.** $(a, a + 1)$ **C.** $(a, a + 2)$ **D.** $(a, a - 1)$

4. How many of the ordered pairs in the data table provided are solutions of the system? $\begin{cases} x + y \le 4 \\ x \ge 1 \end{cases}$

   F. 6   **G.** 10   **H.** 9   **J.** 15

x	y
0	4, 3, 2, 1, 0
1	3, 2, 1, 0
2	2, 1, 0
3	1, 0
4	0

Short Response

5. Is $(4, -2)$ a solution of the system? $\begin{cases} x + y > 2 \\ 2x - y < 1 \end{cases}$

   Explain how you made your determination.

SOLVE IT!

You want to spend no more than $40 for at most 15 tomato plants. You want to maximize the pounds of tomatoes you'll get. How many of each plant should you buy? Justify your answer.

Interactive Exploration

Vocabulary Online

Roma Tomato Plants
Guaranteed tomato yield 8 lb/plant
$2 each

Cherry Tomato Plants
Guaranteed tomato yield 10 lb/plant
$3 each

 Connect Mathematical Ideas (1)(F) How does this problem relate to a problem you have seen before?

Problem 1 **Got It?** **Testing Vertices**

a. Use the following constraints with the objective function $P = x + 3y$. What values of x and y maximize P?

$$\text{Constraints: } \begin{cases} x + 2y \le 5 \\ x - y \le 2 \\ x \ge 0 \\ y \ge 0 \end{cases}$$

Learning Animation

b. Can an objective function $P = ax + by + c$ have the same maximum value at all four vertex points Q, R, S, and T? At points R and S only? Explain using examples.

Problem 2 | **Got It?** | **Using Linear Programming to Maximize Profit**

For the situation in Problem 2, suppose it took you 20 minutes to make a sweatshirt. How many of each type of shirt should you make to maximize your profit?

ELPS Discuss with a classmate. How does reading the tags help you solve this problem? What is the new system of constraints?

Lesson 3-4 | **Linear Programming**

79

Lesson Check

Do you know HOW?

Math Tools

Online Practice

Virtual Nerd Tutorials

1. Graph the system of constraints. Name the vertices of the feasible region.

$$\begin{cases} x + y \leq 6 \\ x \geq 0 \\ y \geq 0 \end{cases}$$

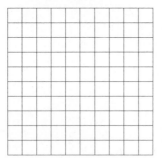

2. Identify the constraints that form the feasible region shown below.

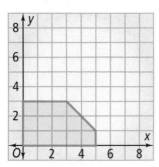

3. Write a system of constraints whose graphs determine a trapezoid. Then find the maximum value of the objective function $P = 10x + 2y$ subject to the set of constraints.

Lesson Check

Do you UNDERSTAND?

Math
Tools

Online
Practice

Virtual Nerd
Tutorials

4. Vocabulary Explain why the inequalities of a linear programming problem are called constraints. (*Hint:* Use the definition of *constraint* as part of your answer.)

5. Select Techniques to Solve Problems (1)(C) Sometimes the coordinates of a vertex of a feasible region will not be whole numbers, when the coordinates of the point where the objective function is maximized must be whole numbers. Is rounding each coordinate to the nearest whole number an appropriate technique in this situation? Why or why not?

6. Connect Mathematical Ideas (1)(F) What are some similarities between solving a linear programming problem and solving a system of linear inequalities? What are some differences?

TEXAS Test Practice

Multiple Choice

For Exercises 1–4, choose the correct letter.

1. You are selling raffle tickets for a fundraiser to both students and their parents. The tickets cost $1 for students and $2 for parents. You know already that at least four students and at least two parents will purchase tickets. You can sell up to a total of 30 tickets. Which of the following is the maximum amount of money you could earn by selling tickets?

   A. $8   **B.** $32   **C.** $56   **D.** $68

2. A feasible region has vertices at $(0, 0)$, $(3, 0)$, $\left(\frac{3}{2}, \frac{7}{2}\right)$, and $(0, 3)$. What are the maximum and minimum values for the objective function $P = 6x + 8y$?

   F. minimum $(0, 0) = 0$
   maximum $\left(\frac{3}{2}, \frac{7}{2}\right) = 37$

   H. minimum $(0, 0) = 14$
   maximum $\left(\frac{3}{2}, \frac{7}{2}\right) = 17$

   G. minimum $(0, 0) = 0$
   maximum $(3, 0) = 24$

   J. minimum $(0, 0) = 0$
   maximum $(0, 3) = 30$

3. Which values of x and y minimize N for the objective function $N = 2x + y$?

   Constraints $\begin{cases} x + y \leq 8 \\ x + 2y \leq 14 \\ x \geq 0, y \geq 0 \end{cases}$

   A. $(0, 0)$ **B.** $(0, 7)$ **C.** $(2, 6)$ **D.** $(8, 0)$

4. Which of the following systems has the vertices $(0, 5)$, $(1, 4)$, $(3, 0)$, and $(0, 0)$?

   F. $\begin{cases} x + y \geq 5 \\ 2x + y \geq 6 \\ x \geq 0, y \geq 0 \end{cases}$ **G.** $\begin{cases} x + y \leq 5 \\ 2x + y \leq 6 \\ x \geq 0, y \geq 0 \end{cases}$ **H.** $\begin{cases} x + y \leq 5 \\ x + 2y \leq 6 \\ x \geq 0, y \geq 0 \end{cases}$ **J.** $\begin{cases} x + y \leq 5 \\ 2x + 2y \leq 6 \\ x \geq 0, y \geq 0 \end{cases}$

Short Response

5. The figure at the right shows the feasible region for a system of constraints. This system includes $x \geq 0$ and $y \geq 0$. What are the remaining constraints? Show your work.

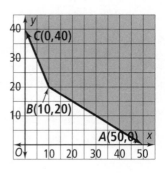

SOLVE IT!

How much does each box weigh? Explain your reasoning.

 Interactive Exploration

 Vocabulary Online

 Use Representations to Communicate Mathematical Ideas (1)(E)
Describe how the representation you used to solve the problem
successfully organizes and communicates your ideas.

Problem 1 | **Got It?** | **Solving a System Using Elimination**

What is the solution of the system? Use elimination. Check your answer in all three original equations.

$$\begin{cases} x - y + z = -1 \\ x + y + 3z = -3 \\ 2x - y + 2z = 0 \end{cases}$$

 Discuss a plan for solving the Got It with a classmate. Ask each other questions such as: How is solving a system with three variables different from solving a system with two variables? Which variable is best to eliminate first, and why? What do you do once that variable is eliminated?

TEKS Process Standard (1)(D)

Problem 2 | **Got It?** | **Solving an Equivalent System**

a. What is the solution of the system? Use elimination.
$$\begin{cases} x - 2y + 3z = 12 \\ 2x - y - 2z = 5 \\ 2x + 2y - z = 4 \end{cases}$$

b. Could you have used elimination in another way? Explain.

Problem 3 | **Got It?** | Solving a System Using Substitution

a. What is the solution of the system? Use substitution.

$$\begin{cases} x - 2y + z = -4 \\ -4x + y - 2z = 1 \\ 2x + 2y - z = 10 \end{cases}$$

 Learning Animation

b. In Problem 3, was it necessary to find the value of z to solve the problem? Explain.

TEKS Process Standard (1)(A)

 Problem 4 | **Got It?** | Solving a Real-World Problem

You can buy T-shirts for $12 each, polo shirts for $24 each, and rugby shirts for $36 each.

Suppose you want to have the same number of T-shirts as polo shirts. Buying 200 shirts with a budget of $5400, how many of each shirt should you buy?

 Learning Animation

Lesson Check

Do you know HOW?

1. Solve the system of equations.

$$\begin{cases} 2y - 3z = 0 \\ x + 3y = -4 \\ 3x + 4y = 3 \end{cases}$$

Math Tools

Online Practice

Virtual Nerd Tutorials

2. Solve the system of equations.

$$\begin{cases} x - \frac{1}{2}y + \frac{1}{2}z = -1 \\ x + 3y - z = 10 \\ \frac{1}{2}x + z = -4 \end{cases}$$

3. The ages of three brothers add up to 38 years. The oldest brother is 5 years older than the youngest brother. Five years ago, the oldest was twice the age of the youngest. Write and solve a system of three equations in three variables to determine the ages of the brothers.

Lesson Check

Do you UNDERSTAND?

4. **Vocabulary** Suppose you are using the elimination method to solve a system of three equations by finding an equivalent system of equations. How will you be able to tell that the system has no solution?

Math Tools

Online Practice

Virtual Nerd Tutorials

5. **Analyze Mathematical Relationships (1)(F)** Without solving either of the two systems, how can you tell that both of these systems have the same solution?

$$\begin{cases} 2x + 3y - 2z = 1 \\ -x - y - 2z = 5 \\ 3x + 2y - 3z = -6 \end{cases} \qquad \begin{cases} 4x + 6y - 4z = 2 \\ -2x - 2y - 4z = 10 \\ 6x + 4y - 6z = -12 \end{cases}$$

6. **Apply Mathematics (1)(A)** Altogether there are 40 pieces of silverware in the drawer. There are twice as many spoons as there are forks and ten fewer knives than there are spoons. How many knives, spoons, and forks are in the drawer?

Gridded Response

Solve each exercise and enter your answer in the grid provided.

1. A change machine contains nickels, dimes, and quarters. There are 75 coins in the machine, and the value of the coins is $7.25. There are 5 times as many nickels as dimes. How many quarters are in the machine?

2. The sum of three numbers is 23. The first number is equal to twice the second number minus 7. The third number is equal to one more than the sum of the first and second numbers. What is the first number?

3. A fish's tail weighs 9 lb. Its head weighs as much as its tail plus half its body. Its body weighs as much as its head and tail. How many pounds does the fish weigh?

4. You are training for a triathlon. In your training routine each week, you bike 5 times as far as you run and run 4 times as far as you swim. One week, you trained a total of 200 miles. How many miles did you swim that week?

1. 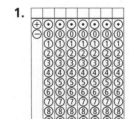 2. 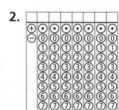 3. 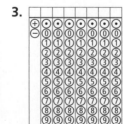 4.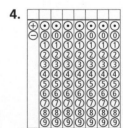

SOLVE IT!

Can you use the rules below to change Figure 1 into Figure 2? Explain.

Interactive Exploration

Vocabulary Online

GAME RULES:

1. You can multiply or divide every number in a row by the same nonzero number.

2. You can add a row to another row, replacing that other row.

 Use a Problem-Solving Model (1)(B) Evaluate your problem-solving model. Which parts were helpful? Which would you want to revise? Explain.

Problem 1 Got It? Identifying a Matrix Element

 Learning Animation

What is element a_{13} in matrix $A = \begin{bmatrix} 4 & -9 & 17 & 1 \\ 0 & 5 & 8 & 6 \\ -3 & -2 & 10 & 0 \end{bmatrix}$?

TEKS Process Standard (1)(E)

 Problem 2 Got It? Representing Systems With Matrices

 Learning Animation

How can you represent each system of equations with a matrix?

a. $\begin{cases} -4x - 2y = 7 \\ 3x + y = -5 \end{cases}$

b. $\begin{cases} 4x - y + 2z = 1 \\ y + 5z = 20 \\ 2x = -y + 7 \end{cases}$

TEKS Process Standard (1)(D)

 Problem 3 Got It? Writing a System From a Matrix

 Learning Animation

What linear system does $\begin{bmatrix} 2 & 0 & | & 6 \\ 5 & -2 & | & 1 \end{bmatrix}$ represent?

Lesson 3-6 | Solving Systems Using Matrices

90

Problem 4 | **Got It?** | Solving a System in Three Variables Using a Matrix

Learning Animation

a. What is the solution of the system?

$$\begin{cases} x - 3y - z = -9 \\ 3x - 7y + z = -9 \\ -2x + 3y = 7 \end{cases}$$

b. Explain how the solution of the system represented by this matrix can be found without performing any further operations on the matrix.

$$\begin{bmatrix} 1 & 2 & -3 & | & 7 \\ 0 & 1 & -4 & | & -6 \\ 0 & 0 & 1 & | & 3 \end{bmatrix}$$

 Problem 5 | **Got It?** | Using a Calculator to Solve a Linear System

Learning Animation

What is the solution of the system of equations?

$$\begin{cases} a + 4b + 6c = 21 \\ 2a - 2b + c = 4 \\ -8b + c = -1 \end{cases}$$

ELPS Share information in a group to solve this problem. How do you know how many rows and columns the matrix will have? What do you do when a variable is not represented in an equation? What matrix represents the system in this problem? What feature do you use on your calculator to solve matrices?

Lesson Check

Do you know HOW?

**Math
Tools**

**Online
Practice**

**Virtual Nerd
Tutorials**

1. Write a matrix to represent the system. $\begin{cases} x + 3y - z = 2 \\ x + 2z = 8 \\ 2y - z = 1 \end{cases}$

2. Identify the dimensions of the matrix representing the system, and then write the matrix.

$$\begin{cases} -2w + 3x - 3y = 2 \\ 4w - x + 2z = 8 \\ 3x - 2y + z = 1 \\ w + 2y - z = 6 \end{cases}$$

3. Solve the system using a matrix. $\begin{cases} 2z + 3y - 14 = x \\ 4y - 27 + 2z - 6x = 0 \\ -10.5 = 3x - 2y + z \end{cases}$

Lesson Check

Do you UNDERSTAND?

Math Tools

4. **Vocabulary** Describe the difference in identifying element a_{21} and a_{12} in the matrix below.

$$\begin{bmatrix} 4 & -9 & 17 & 1 \\ 0 & 5 & 8 & 6 \\ -3 & -2 & 10 & 0 \end{bmatrix}$$

Online Practice

Virtual Nerd Tutorials

5. **Create Representations to Communicate Mathematical Ideas (1)(E)**
Your family paid a total of $8 for 4 students and 2 adults to attend a school play. Your friend's family paid a total of $5 for 1 adult and 3 students. Write a matrix that models this situation.

6. **Analyze Mathematical Relationships (1)(F)** Explain how you know that these two matrices represent equivalent linear systems.

$$\begin{bmatrix} 1 & 1 & 1 & | & 2 \\ 2 & 1 & 1 & | & 1 \\ 1 & -1 & 1 & | & -2 \end{bmatrix} \qquad \begin{bmatrix} 2 & 1 & 1 & | & 1 \\ 1 & 1 & 1 & | & 2 \\ -1 & 1 & -1 & | & 2 \end{bmatrix}$$

TEXAS Test Practice

Multiple Choice

For Exercises 1–3, choose the correct letter.

1. A manufacturer sells packages of costume jewelry containing bracelets and necklaces. A package of 5 bracelets and 1 necklace costs $7, and a package of 2 bracelets and 3 necklaces costs $8. Which matrix represents the system of equations that models this situation?

   A. $\begin{bmatrix} 5 & 1 & | & 7 \\ 2 & 3 & | & 8 \end{bmatrix}$

   B. $\begin{bmatrix} 5 & -1 & | & 7 \\ 2 & -3 & | & 8 \end{bmatrix}$

   C. $\begin{bmatrix} 5 & | & 2 \\ 1 & | & 3 \\ 7 & | & 8 \end{bmatrix}$

   D. $\begin{bmatrix} 5 & 7 & | & 1 \\ 2 & 8 & | & 3 \end{bmatrix}$

2. What is the solution of the system represented by the matrix $\begin{bmatrix} 2 & 3 & -1 & | & 2 \\ -3 & -4 & 2 & | & -2 \\ 1 & 2 & -1 & | & 3 \end{bmatrix}$?

   F. $(1, 3, 4)$

   G. $(4, -3, 1)$

   H. $(-4, 3, -1)$

   J. $(3, -4, -1)$

3. Which one of the four systems of equations below, represented in matrix form, does not have the same set of solutions as the system $\begin{cases} x + 2y = 1 \\ 3x - y = 6 \end{cases}$?

   A. $\begin{bmatrix} 2 & 4 & | & 2 \\ 3 & -1 & | & 6 \end{bmatrix}$

   B. $\begin{bmatrix} 3 & -1 & | & 6 \\ 1 & 2 & | & 1 \end{bmatrix}$

   C. $\begin{bmatrix} 4 & 1 & | & 7 \\ 3 & -1 & | & 6 \end{bmatrix}$

   D. $\begin{bmatrix} 1 & 4 & | & 1 \\ 3 & -2 & | & 6 \end{bmatrix}$

Short Response

4. A clothing store is having a sale. A pair of jeans costs $15, and a shirt costs $8. You spend $131 and buy a total of 12 items. Using a matrix, how many pairs of jeans and shirts do you buy? Show your work.

SOLVE IT!

How can you complete the squares to show number patterns in each square, and from square to square? Explain each pattern.

	2	
4		6
	8	

2		6
	10	
14		18

	6	9
	15	18

16	20	
28	32	

	25	

Interactive Exploration

Vocabulary Online

Analyze Mathematical Relationships (1)(F) What mathematical relationships did you identify in the problem? How did you use them to solve the problem?

Problem 1 **Got It?** **Adding and Subtracting Matrices**

Learning
Animation

Given $A = \begin{bmatrix} -12 & 24 \\ -3 & 5 \\ -1 & 10 \end{bmatrix}$ and $B = \begin{bmatrix} -3 & 1 \\ 2 & -4 \\ -1 & 5 \end{bmatrix}$, what are the following?

a. $A + B$

b. $A - B$

c. Is matrix addition commutative? Explain.

 Read and discuss part (c) with a classmate. What do you think the question is asking? Add $A + B$ and then $B + A$. Do you get the same solution? Next subtract $A - B$ and then $B - A$. Compare the results.

TEKS Process Standard (1)(A)

 Problem 2 **Got It?** **Solving a Matrix Equation**

Learning
Animation

If $B = \begin{bmatrix} 1 & 6 & -1 \\ 2 & 6 & 1 \\ -1 & -2 & 4 \end{bmatrix}$, $C = \begin{bmatrix} 2 & 0 & 0 \\ -1 & -3 & 6 \\ 2 & 3 & -1 \end{bmatrix}$, and $A - B = C$, what is A?

Lesson 4-1 │ Adding and Subtracting Matrices

Problem 3 | **Got It?** | Using Identity and Opposite Matrices

What are the following sums?

a. $\begin{bmatrix} 14 & 5 \\ 0 & -2 \end{bmatrix} + \begin{bmatrix} -14 & -5 \\ 0 & 2 \end{bmatrix}$

Learning Animation

b. $\begin{bmatrix} 0 & 0 & 0 \\ 0 & 0 & 0 \end{bmatrix} + \begin{bmatrix} -1 & 10 & -5 \\ 0 & 2 & -3 \end{bmatrix}$

Problem 4 | **Got It?** | Finding Unknown Matrix Values

What values of x, y, and z make the following equations true?

a. $\begin{bmatrix} x+3 & -2 \\ y-1 & x+1 \end{bmatrix} = \begin{bmatrix} 9 & -2 \\ 2y+5 & 7 \end{bmatrix}$

Learning Animation

b. $\begin{bmatrix} z & -3 \\ 3x & 0 \end{bmatrix} - \begin{bmatrix} 10 & -4 \\ x & 2y+6 \end{bmatrix} = \begin{bmatrix} 2 & 1 \\ 8 & 4y+12 \end{bmatrix}$

Lesson Check

Do you know HOW?

For Exercises 1–3, use the matrices below.

$$A = \begin{bmatrix} 2 & 3 & -1 \\ 0 & 2 & 1 \end{bmatrix} \qquad B = \begin{bmatrix} -3 & 2 & 1 \\ 3 & 0 & 5 \end{bmatrix}$$

1. Find the difference $A - B$.

2. Find the sum $A + A$.

3. Solve the equation $A - X = B - A$ for X.

Math
Tools

Online
Practice

Virtual Nerd
Tutorials

Lesson Check

Do you UNDERSTAND?

4. **Vocabulary** Explain how you know that $[2 \quad -5 \quad 7]$ is the additive inverse of $[-2 \quad 5 \quad -7]$, based on the corresponding elements of the matrices.

Math Tools

Online Practice

Virtual Nerd Tutorials

5. **Analyze Mathematical Relationships (1)(F)** Are the two matrices equal? Explain.

$$\begin{bmatrix} \frac{1}{2} & \frac{3}{8} \\ 0.2 & \sqrt{16} \end{bmatrix} \text{ and } \begin{bmatrix} 0.5 & 0.375 \\ \frac{1}{5} & 4 \end{bmatrix}$$

6. **Use Representations to Communicate Mathematical Ideas (1)(E)**
   Use three 2×2 matrices to verify the Associative Property of Addition.

TEXAS Test Practice

Multiple Choice

For Exercises 1–4, choose the correct letter.

1. Siblings Jenna and Brandon each spend a few hours each week doing household chores, as documented in the table. Which matrix represents the total number of hours spent vacuuming and doing laundry (by either Jenna or Brandon) in a week?

Hours Per Week Spent Doing Chores

	Jenna	Brandon
Vacuuming	3	1
Laundry	2	4

A. $\begin{bmatrix} 2 \\ -2 \end{bmatrix}$ B. $\begin{bmatrix} 4 \\ 6 \end{bmatrix}$ C. $\begin{bmatrix} 2 \\ 2 \end{bmatrix}$ D. $\begin{bmatrix} 3 \\ 4 \end{bmatrix}$

2. Which matrix is equivalent to X in the equation $\begin{bmatrix} 4 & 0 \\ 1 & -2 \end{bmatrix} + X = \begin{bmatrix} -2 & 0 \\ 1 & 4 \end{bmatrix}$?

F. $\begin{bmatrix} -6 & 0 \\ 0 & 6 \end{bmatrix}$ G. $\begin{bmatrix} 2 & 0 \\ 0 & 2 \end{bmatrix}$ H. $\begin{bmatrix} 2 & 0 \\ 2 & 2 \end{bmatrix}$ J. $\begin{bmatrix} 6 & 0 \\ 0 & -6 \end{bmatrix}$

3. Which matrix is equivalent to P in the equation $\begin{bmatrix} 7 & 8 \\ 9 & 10 \\ 11 & 12 \end{bmatrix} - P = \begin{bmatrix} 0 & 0 \\ 0 & 0 \\ 0 & 0 \end{bmatrix}$?

A. $\begin{bmatrix} 0 & 0 \\ 0 & 0 \\ 0 & 0 \end{bmatrix}$ B. $\begin{bmatrix} -1 & -1 \\ -1 & -1 \\ -1 & -1 \end{bmatrix}$ C. $\begin{bmatrix} -7 & -8 \\ -9 & -10 \\ -11 & -12 \end{bmatrix}$ D. $\begin{bmatrix} 7 & 8 \\ 9 & 10 \\ 11 & 12 \end{bmatrix}$

4. For nonzero constants a and b, what matrix is equivalent to X in the equation $\begin{bmatrix} a & 1 \\ 0 & \frac{a}{b} \end{bmatrix} + X = \begin{bmatrix} 2a & 0 \\ 0 & 1 \end{bmatrix}$?

F. $\begin{bmatrix} 2 & -1 \\ 0 & \frac{b}{a} \end{bmatrix}$ G. $\begin{bmatrix} a & -1 \\ 0 & \frac{b}{a} \end{bmatrix}$ H. $\begin{bmatrix} a & 0 \\ 0 & 1-\frac{a}{b} \end{bmatrix}$ J. $\begin{bmatrix} a & -1 \\ 0 & 1-\frac{a}{b} \end{bmatrix}$

Short Response

5. If $\begin{bmatrix} 8 & 2x-1 \\ 2y+1 & 3 \end{bmatrix} = \begin{bmatrix} 8 & -7 \\ y & -x \end{bmatrix}$, what values of x and y make the equation true? Show your work.

SOLVE IT!

In a family of five, the parents are on a 2000-calorie diet. The three children are on a 2500-calorie diet. For a dessert, the family shares a 500-g cake with 20% fat content. What percentage of the entire family's daily fat allowance is in the cake?

Interactive Exploration

Vocabulary Online

	Calories	2,000	2,500
Total Fat	Less than	65 g	80 g
Sat Fat	Less than	20 g	25 g
Cholesterol	Less than	300 mg	300 mg
Sodium	Less than	2,400 mg	2,400 mg
Total Carbohydrate		300 g	375 g
Dietary Fiber		25 g	30 g

 Apply Mathematics (1)(A) Describe another real-world situation for which you could apply the same mathematical model.

Problem 1 | **Got It?** | Using Scalar Products

Learning Animation

If $A = \begin{bmatrix} 2 & 8 & -3 \\ -1 & 5 & 2 \end{bmatrix}$ and $B = \begin{bmatrix} -1 & 0 & 5 \\ 0 & 3 & -2 \end{bmatrix}$, what is $3A - 2B$?

TEKS Process Standard (1)(F)

 Problem 2 | **Got It?** | Solving a Matrix Equation With Scalars

Learning Animation

What is the solution of $3X - 2\begin{bmatrix} -1 & 5 \\ 7 & 0 \end{bmatrix} = \begin{bmatrix} 17 & -13 \\ -7 & 0 \end{bmatrix}$?

 Problem 3 | **Got It?** | Multiplying Matrices

Learning Animation

If $A = \begin{bmatrix} 2 & -1 \\ 3 & 4 \end{bmatrix}$ and $B = \begin{bmatrix} -3 & 1 \\ 0 & 2 \end{bmatrix}$, what are the following products?

a. AB 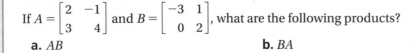 **b.** BA

c. Is matrix multiplication commutative? Explain.

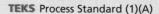

TEKS Process Standard (1)(A)

Problem 4 | **Got It?** | Applying Matrix Multiplication

There are three ways to score in a basketball game: three-point field goals, two-point field goals, and one-point free throws. In 1994, suppose a high school player scored 36 two-point field goals and 28 free throws. In 2006, suppose a high school player scored 7 three-point field goals, 21 two-point field goals, and 18 free throws. Using matrix multiplication, how many points did each player score?

 Discuss the game of basketball with a classmate. Draw a basketball court, labeling the 3-point, 2-point, and free throw areas with the numbers 3, 2, and 1. Build a matrix P for possible scoring points and a matrix S for the players' scores. How can you use P and S to find the total points for each player?

TEKS Process Standard (1)(D)

Problem 5 | **Got It?** | Determining Whether Product Matrices Exist

Do the following products exist?

$$A = \begin{bmatrix} 1 & 4 \\ -3 & 5 \end{bmatrix} \qquad B = \begin{bmatrix} -1 & 1 \end{bmatrix} \qquad C = \begin{bmatrix} 4 & 2 & 0 \\ 1 & 3 & 5 \end{bmatrix}$$

a. AB

b. BA

c. AC

d. CA

e. BC

Lesson Check

Do you know HOW?

1. Write the matrix $3A - 2B$, where $A = \begin{bmatrix} 3 & -1 \\ 2 & 0 \end{bmatrix}$ and $B = \begin{bmatrix} 1 & 3 \\ -2 & 2 \end{bmatrix}$.

2. Let $A = \begin{bmatrix} 2 & 0 & 0 \\ 0 & 2 & 0 \\ 0 & 0 & 2 \end{bmatrix}$ and $B = \begin{bmatrix} 1 & 2 & 3 \\ 0 & 1 & 2 \\ 0 & 0 & 1 \end{bmatrix}$. Find the matrix $A(B + A)$.

3. Use the matrices A and B in Exercise 2 to verify the Distributive Property by showing that $A(B + A) = AB + AA$.

Math Tools

Online Practice

Virtual Nerd Tutorials

Lesson Check

Do you UNDERSTAND?

Math Tools

Online Practice

Virtual Nerd Tutorials

4. Vocabulary Which type of multiplication, *scalar* or *matrix*, can help you with a repeated matrix addition problem? Explain.

5. Analyze Mathematical Relationships (1)(F) Suppose A is a 2×3 matrix, B is a 2×2 matrix, and C is a 3×3 matrix. Give the dimensions of each product if it exists. If the product is not defined, label it *undefined*.

a. AB **b.** AC

c. BC **d.** BA

6. Use Representations to Communicate Mathematical Ideas (1)(E)

When you perform the multiplication $\begin{bmatrix} w & x \\ y & z \end{bmatrix}\begin{bmatrix} 0 & 1 \\ 1 & 0 \end{bmatrix}$, the result is $\begin{bmatrix} x & w \\ z & y \end{bmatrix}$, which is the original matrix with the columns switched. How does the multiplication $\begin{bmatrix} 0 & 1 \\ 1 & 0 \end{bmatrix}\begin{bmatrix} w & x \\ y & z \end{bmatrix}$ modify the original matrix?

TEXAS Test Practice

Multiple Choice

For Exercises 1–3, choose the correct letter.

1. The following table shows how many hours per week Peter spends doing reading or homework in his biology and English classes. He decides to increase the number of hours he spends reading or doing homework by 50% in both subjects. Which matrix represents the amount of hours per week he spends on this schoolwork after making that change?

Hours Per Week Spent on Biology or English Schoolwork

	Biology	English
Reading	5	6
Doing homework	2	3

A. $\begin{bmatrix} 10 & 12 \\ 4 & 6 \end{bmatrix}$
B. $\begin{bmatrix} 7.5 & 9 \\ 3 & 4.5 \end{bmatrix}$
C. $\begin{bmatrix} 5 & 6 \\ 2 & 3 \end{bmatrix}$
D. $\begin{bmatrix} 2 & 3 \\ 5 & 6 \end{bmatrix}$

2. What is the product $\begin{bmatrix} 6 & -1 \\ 3 & 9 \end{bmatrix}\begin{bmatrix} 3 \\ -6 \end{bmatrix}$?

F. $\begin{bmatrix} 18 & -3 \\ -18 & -54 \end{bmatrix}$
G. $\begin{bmatrix} 24 & -45 \end{bmatrix}$
H. $\begin{bmatrix} 24 \\ -45 \end{bmatrix}$
J. $\begin{bmatrix} 15 & 36 \\ -30 & -72 \end{bmatrix}$

3. Which matrix is the solution of $\begin{bmatrix} 1 & -1 & 2 \\ 2 & 0 & -1 \end{bmatrix} - 2X = \begin{bmatrix} 4 & 5 & 6 \\ 6 & 5 & 4 \end{bmatrix}$?

A. $\begin{bmatrix} 3 & 6 & 4 \\ 4 & 5 & 5 \end{bmatrix}$

C. $\begin{bmatrix} \frac{3}{2} & 3 & 2 \\ 2 & \frac{5}{2} & \frac{5}{2} \end{bmatrix}$

B. $\begin{bmatrix} -6 & -12 & -8 \\ -8 & -10 & -10 \end{bmatrix}$

D. $\begin{bmatrix} -\frac{3}{2} & -3 & -2 \\ -2 & -\frac{5}{2} & -\frac{5}{2} \end{bmatrix}$

Extended Response

4. The table shows the number of tiles used in a house. Blue tiles cost $1.20 each, white tiles cost $1.50 each, and green tiles cost $.80 each. Write and solve a matrix equation to find the total cost of the tiles. Show your work.

Tiles Used

	Blue	White	Green
Bath #1	20	50	10
Bath #2	15	30	5
Kitchen	25	100	50

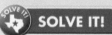

SOLVE IT!

What is the area of the triangle? Explain how you found your answer.

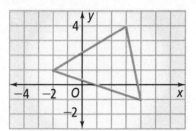

Interactive
Exploration

Vocabulary
Online

 Select Techniques to Solve Problems (1)(C) What other techniques could you use
to solve the problem? Select one and explain how you would use it.

Problem 1 **Got It?** Determining Whether Matrices Are Inverses

Learning Animation

For each of the following, are A and B inverses?

a. $A = \begin{bmatrix} 1 & 1 \\ 5 & 4 \end{bmatrix}$ $B = \begin{bmatrix} -4 & 1 \\ 5 & -1 \end{bmatrix}$

b. $A = \begin{bmatrix} 3 & 2 \\ 5 & 4 \end{bmatrix}$ $B = \begin{bmatrix} 2 & -1 \\ -\frac{5}{2} & \frac{3}{2} \end{bmatrix}$

c. Does the matrix $\begin{bmatrix} 0 & 0 \\ 0 & 0 \end{bmatrix}$ have an inverse? Explain.

 Problem 2 **Got It?** Evaluating the Determinants of Matrices

Learning Animation

What are the determinants of the following matrices?

a. $\begin{bmatrix} 3 & 6 \\ 2 & 5 \end{bmatrix}$

b. $\begin{bmatrix} -2 & 0 \\ 3 & 0 \end{bmatrix}$

c. $\begin{bmatrix} 1 & 0 & 3 \\ 2 & 4 & 6 \\ 5 & -1 & 3 \end{bmatrix}$

TEKS Process Standard (1)(A)

 Problem 3 **Got It?** Finding the Area of a Polygon

Learning Animation

What is the area of the triangle with the given vertices?

a. $(1, 3), (-3, 0), (5, 0)$

b. $(1, 3), (5, 8), (9, -1)$

TEKS Process Standard (1)(C)

 Problem 4 **Got It?** Finding the Inverse of a Matrix

Does the matrix have an inverse? If so, what is it?

a. $A = \begin{bmatrix} 4 & 2 \\ 3 & 2 \end{bmatrix}$ **b.** $B = \begin{bmatrix} 2 & 5 \\ -4 & -10 \end{bmatrix}$ **c.** $C = \begin{bmatrix} 7 & 4 \\ 5 & 3 \end{bmatrix}$

Learning Animation

TEKS Process Standard (1)(E)

Problem 5 **Got It?** Encoding and Decoding With Matrices

a. How can you use matrix multiplication and the coding matrix $\begin{bmatrix} 4 & 8 \\ -2 & 4 \end{bmatrix}$ to encode the credit card number 4173 1234 9876 1357?

Learning Animation

b. How can you use the inverse of the coding matrix to recover the credit card number?

ELPS Read and discuss part (a) with a classmate. What is a code? What does the prefix *en* mean? What do you think it means to *encode* something? What must you do to *encode* the credit card number?

Lesson Check

Do you know HOW?

1. Evaluate the determinant of the matrix $\begin{bmatrix} 4 & -1 \\ 8 & 2 \end{bmatrix}$.

Math
Tools

Online
Practice

Virtual Nerd
Tutorials

2. Find the inverse of the matrix $\begin{bmatrix} 5 & 2 \\ 7 & 3 \end{bmatrix}$, if it exists.

3. Find the value of a that makes the matrix $\begin{bmatrix} a & 2 \\ a+1 & 1 \end{bmatrix}$ singular.

Lesson Check

Do you UNDERSTAND?

4. Vocabulary Can there exist a multiplicative identity matrix whose dimensions are 2×3?

5. Select Techniques to Solve Problems (1)(C) Your friend calculates that the determinant of $A = \begin{bmatrix} 2 & 5 \\ -3 & 1 \end{bmatrix}$ is -13. Without calculating the determinant yourself, how can you use a matrix inverse to check whether your friend is correct?

6. Explain Mathematical Ideas (1)(G) Explain why a matrix in the form $\begin{bmatrix} a & a^2 \\ 1 & a \end{bmatrix}$ does not have an inverse.

TEXAS Test Practice

Gridded Response

Solve each exercise and enter your answer in the grid provided.

1. Use matrices to find the area of a triangle with vertices at $(-5, 0)$, $(3, -1)$, and $(2, 6)$.

2. If $A = \begin{bmatrix} 2 & 1 \\ -9 & 3 \end{bmatrix}$ and the inverse of A is $x \cdot \begin{bmatrix} 3 & -1 \\ 9 & 2 \end{bmatrix}$, what is the value of x?

3. If $A = \begin{bmatrix} 6 & 2 \\ 4 & 1 \end{bmatrix}$ and $A^{-1} = \begin{bmatrix} x & 1 \\ 2 & -3 \end{bmatrix}$, what is the value of x?

4. If the determinant of $\begin{bmatrix} a & 0 \\ 1 & a \end{bmatrix}$ equals 9 and a is non-negative, what is the value of a?

1. 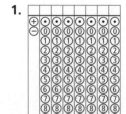   **2.** 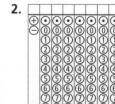   **3.** 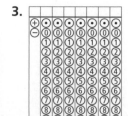   **4.**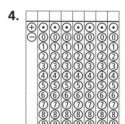

SOLVE IT!

The machine counted your nickels and dimes. How many of each coin did you have? Explain.

Coins Counted.........184
Cash Value....... $14.35

Interactive Exploration

Vocabulary Online

 Explain Mathematical Ideas (1)(G) A classmate questions your solution to the problem. Use precise mathematical language to explain why your solution is correct.

TEKS Process Standard (1)(C)

 Problem 1 | **Got It?** | **Solving a Matrix Equation Using an Inverse Matrix**

Learning Animation

What is the solution of each matrix equation?

a. $\begin{bmatrix} 4 & 3 \\ 2 & 2 \end{bmatrix} X = \begin{bmatrix} -5 \\ 2 \end{bmatrix}$ **b.** $\begin{bmatrix} 7 & 5 \\ 4 & 3 \end{bmatrix} X = \begin{bmatrix} -3 & 0 \\ 1 & 4 \end{bmatrix}$ **c.** $\begin{bmatrix} 2 & 3 \\ 4 & 6 \end{bmatrix} X = \begin{bmatrix} 3 \\ -7 \end{bmatrix}$

 Problem 2 | **Got It?** | **Writing a System as a Matrix Equation**

Learning Animation

What is the matrix equation that corresponds to each system?

a. $\begin{cases} 3x - 7y = 8 \\ 5x + y = -2 \end{cases}$

b. $\begin{cases} x + 3y + 5z = 12 \\ -2x + y - 4z = -2 \\ 7x - 2y = 7 \end{cases}$

c. $\begin{cases} 2x + 3 = 8y \\ -x + y = -4 \end{cases}$

TEKS Process Standard (1)(C)

 Problem 3 | **Got It?** | Solving a System of Two Equations

Learning Animation

What is the solution of each system of equations? Solve using matrices.

a. $\begin{cases} 9x + 2y = 3 \\ 3x + y = -6 \end{cases}$

b. $\begin{cases} 4x - 6y = 9 \\ -10x + 15y = 8 \end{cases}$

TEKS Process Standard (1)(A)

 Problem 4 | **Got It?** | Solving a System of Three Equations

Learning Animation

After following her exercise program from Problem 4 for a month, your friend plans to increase the calories she burns with each session. She still wants to exercise for 40 min every other day, but now she wants to burn 460 calories during each session. If she only runs and jogs, how many minutes of each exercise type should she do now?

Calories Burned

Running (8 mi/h)	Jogging (5 mi/h)	Walking (3.5 mi/h)
12.5 cal/min	7.5 cal/min	3.5 cal/min

ELPS Read and summarize the information in the Got It with a classmate. What information stays the same and what changes from Problem 4? What is the new equation for the number of calories burned? What is the new equation for the time spent exercising?

Lesson Check

Do you know HOW?

Math
Tools

Online
Practice

Virtual Nerd
Tutorials

1. Write the system as a matrix equation.

$$\begin{cases} 2x + 3y = 12 \\ x - 2y + z = 9 \\ 6y - 4z = 8 \end{cases}$$

2. Write the matrix equation as a system of linear equations and use a determinant to explain why the system has no unique solution.

$$\begin{bmatrix} -2 & 3 \\ 4 & -6 \end{bmatrix} \begin{bmatrix} a \\ b \end{bmatrix} = \begin{bmatrix} 2 \\ -5 \end{bmatrix}$$

3. Use a calculator to find the inverse of the matrix $\begin{bmatrix} 1 & 1 & 1 \\ 0 & 1 & 1 \\ 0 & 0 & 1 \end{bmatrix}$ and use the

inverse to solve the system $\begin{bmatrix} 1 & 1 & 1 \\ 0 & 1 & 1 \\ 0 & 0 & 1 \end{bmatrix} \begin{bmatrix} x \\ y \\ z \end{bmatrix} = \begin{bmatrix} 1 \\ 2 \\ 3 \end{bmatrix}$.

Lesson Check

Do you know UNDERSTAND?

Math Tools

Online Practice

Virtual Nerd Tutorials

4. Analyze Mathematical Relationships (1)(F) What determines the dimensions of the variable matrix in a matrix equation representing a system of linear equations?

5. Evaluate Reasonableness (1)(B) A student is trying to use matrices to solve the matrix equation $AX = B$. The student writes $X = BA^{-1}$. Do you agree or disagree? Explain.

6. Explain Mathematical Ideas (1)(G) A student claims that if the coefficient matrix in a matrix equation has no inverse, then the system of equations represented by the matrix equation has no solutions. Do you agree or disagree? Explain.

TEXAS Test Practice

Multiple Choice

For Exercises 1–4, choose the correct letter.

1. A teacher is counting how many spare pencils and erasers he has. He has twice as many erasers as pencils and a total of 21 items altogether. Which matrix equation represents the system that is given by this situation?

   A. $\begin{bmatrix} 1 & 1 \\ 2 & -1 \end{bmatrix}\begin{bmatrix} p \\ e \end{bmatrix} = \begin{bmatrix} 21 \\ 0 \end{bmatrix}$

   C. $\begin{bmatrix} 1 & 21 \\ 2 & -1 \end{bmatrix}\begin{bmatrix} 1 \\ 1 \end{bmatrix} = \begin{bmatrix} p \\ e \end{bmatrix}$

   B. $\begin{bmatrix} 1 & 1 \\ 2 & -1 \end{bmatrix}\begin{bmatrix} 21 \\ 0 \end{bmatrix} = \begin{bmatrix} p \\ e \end{bmatrix}$

   D. $\begin{bmatrix} 1 & 21 \\ 2 & 0 \end{bmatrix}\begin{bmatrix} p \\ e \end{bmatrix} = \begin{bmatrix} 1 \\ 0 \end{bmatrix}$

2. Let $\begin{bmatrix} 3 & 5 \\ -4 & -1 \end{bmatrix}\begin{bmatrix} x \\ y \end{bmatrix} = \begin{bmatrix} -4 \\ -6 \end{bmatrix}$. What values of x and y make the equation true?

   F. $(-12, -1)$ G. $(-4, -6)$ H. $(-3, -20)$ J. $(2, -2)$

3. Each one of the following systems represents two lines on the coordinate plane. If the lines were graphed, which pair of lines would intersect at one point only? Use matrices.

   A. $\begin{cases} 3x - 2y = 43 \\ 9x - 6y = 40 \end{cases}$

   C. $\begin{cases} 2x - 5y = 6 \\ 4x + 7y = 12 \end{cases}$

   B. $\begin{cases} 6x + 8y = 16 \\ -3x - 4y = 12 \end{cases}$

   D. $\begin{cases} 4x + 2y = 10 \\ 8x + 4y = 18 \end{cases}$

4. Let $\begin{bmatrix} 5 & 1 \\ 2 & -1 \end{bmatrix} X = \begin{bmatrix} 0 \\ -14 \end{bmatrix}$. What value of X makes the equation true?

   F. $\begin{bmatrix} -2 \\ 10 \end{bmatrix}$ G. $\begin{bmatrix} -6 \\ -15 \end{bmatrix}$ H. $\begin{bmatrix} 0 \\ 14 \end{bmatrix}$ J. $\begin{bmatrix} -5 \\ 2 \end{bmatrix}$

Short Response

5. The Spirit Club sold buttons for $1, hats for $4, and T-shirts for $8. They sold 3 times as many buttons as hats. Together, the number of hats and T-shirts sold was equal to the number of buttons sold. They earned a total of $460. Write and solve a matrix equation to find how many buttons, hats, and T-shirts the club sold.

SOLVE IT!

In the computer game Steeplechase, you press the "jump" button and the horse makes the jump shown. The highest part of the jump must be directly above the fence or you lose time. Where should this horse be when you press "jump"? Explain your reasoning.

Interactive Exploration

Vocabulary Online

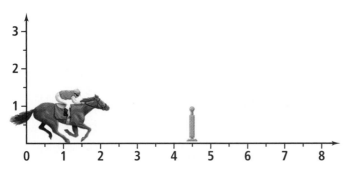

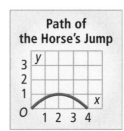

Path of the Horse's Jump

 Apply Mathematics (1)(A) Describe another real-world situation for which you could apply the same mathematical model.

TEKS Process Standard (1)(D)

 Problem 1 | **Got It?** | Graphing a Function of the Form $f(x) = ax^2$

a. What is the graph of $f(x) = -\frac{1}{3}x^2$?

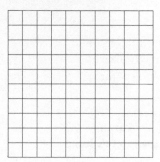

 Learning Animation

b. What can you say about the graph of the function $f(x) = ax^2$ if a is a negative number? Explain.

 Problem 2 | **Got It?** | Graphing Translations of $f(x) = x^2$

Graph each function. How is it a translation of $f(x) = x^2$?

Learning Animation

a. $g(x) = x^2 + 3$

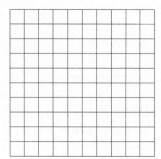

b. $h(x) = (x + 1)^2$

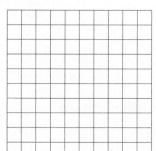

Lesson 5-1 | Attributes and Transformations of Quadratic Functions

TEKS Process Standard (1)(G)

 Problem 3 **Got It?** **Interpreting Vertex Form**

What are the vertex, axis of symmetry, minimum or maximum, and domain and range of the function $y = -2(x + 1)^2 + 4$?

Learning Animation

ELPS Read and discuss the vocabulary from the Got It with a classmate. Write the following words, *symmetry*, *maximum*, and *minimum*, on flash cards and practice reading and pronouncing them with a classmate. Draw a parabola and point to the vertex. Tell how just looking at the vertex form of an equation can help you determine the axis of symmetry, maximum or minimum, domain, and range.

 Problem 4 **Got It?** **Using Vertex Form**

What steps transform the graph of $y = x^2$ to $y = 2(x + 2)^2 - 5$?

Learning Animation

 Problem 5 **Got It?** **Writing a Quadratic Function in Vertex Form**

In problem 5, the vertex of the dolphin's jump was (3, 7). Suppose the path of the jump changes so that the axis of symmetry becomes $x = 2$ and the height stays the same. If the path of the jump also passes through the point (5, 5), what quadratic function would model this path?

Learning Animation

Lesson 5-1 │ **Attributes and Transformations of Quadratic Functions**

Do you know HOW?

Math
Tools

Online
Practice

Virtual Nerd
Tutorials

1. Graph the function $f(x) = -3x^2 - 3$.

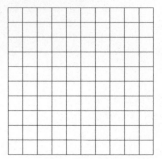

2. Write the quadratic function that is a translation 2 units up and 3 units to the left of the function $y = -2x^2 + 35$.

3. Determine whether the function $f(x) = 0.25(2x - 15)^2 + 10$ has a maximum or a minimum value. Identify this minimum or maximum value of the function. Explain your reasoning.

Lesson Check

Do you UNDERSTAND?

Math Tools

Online Practice

Virtual Nerd Tutorials

4. **Vocabulary** When does the graph of a quadratic function have a minimum value?

5. **Explain Mathematical Ideas (1)(G)** Is $y = 0(x - 4)^2 + 3$ a quadratic function? Explain.

6. **Analyze Mathematical Relationships (1)(F)** What are the differences between the graphs of $y = (x + 6)^2$ and $y = (x - 6)^2 + 7$?

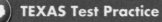

TEXAS Test Practice

Multiple Choice

For Exercises 1–4, choose the correct letter.

1. A dip in a roller coaster track is modeled by the function $y = 3(x - 7)^2 + 4$. What is the lowest point of the dip, as represented by the vertex of the function?

    A. $(-7, -4)$ **B.** $(-7, 4)$ **C.** $(7, -4)$ **D.** $(7, 4)$

2. Which is the graph of the function $f(x) = -2(x + 3)^2$ after it has been translated 5 units up?

F.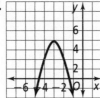

H.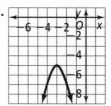

G.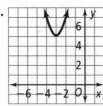

J.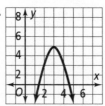

3. Which of the following best describes how to transform $y = x^2$ to the graph of $y = 4(x - 2.5)^2 - 3$?

    A. Translate 2.5 units left, stretch by a factor of 4, translate 3 units down.

    B. Translate 3 units right and 2.5 units down, stretch by a factor of 4.

    C. Translate 2.5 units right, stretch by a factor of 4, translate 3 units down.

    D. Stretch by a factor of 4, translate 2.5 units left and 3 units down.

4. What is the equation of the parabola with vertex $(-4, 6)$ passing through the point $(-2, a)$?

    F. $y = \frac{a - 6}{4}(x - 4)^2 + 6$ **H.** $y = \frac{a - 6}{4}(x - 4)^2 - 6$

    G. $y = \frac{a - 6}{4}(x + 4)^2 + 6$ **J.** $y = \frac{a - 3}{2}(x + 4)^2 + 6$

Short Response

5. A baseball is hit so that its height above ground is given by the equation $h = -16t^2 + 96t + 4$, where h is the height in feet and t is the time in seconds after it is hit. Show your work.

    a. How long does it take the baseball to reach its highest point?

    b. How high will it go?

Scan page for an interactive
version of this Solve It.

SOLVE IT!

You and a friend are tossing a ball back and forth. You each toss and catch the ball at waist level, 3 feet high. What type of function models the path of the ball? What is an equation, in standard form, for each toss? Explain your reasoning. How do the equations compare?

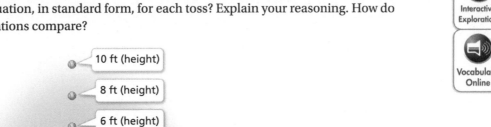

10 ft (height)

8 ft (height)

6 ft (height)

10 ft

Interactive Exploration

Vocabulary Online

Use Multiple Representations to Communicate Mathematical Ideas (1)(D)
What is another representation you could use to present your solution? Explain how the representation communicates the same information.

TEKS Process Standard (1)(E)

 Problem 1 | **Got It?** | Writing an Equation of a Parabola

Learning Animation

What is the equation of a parabola containing the points $(0, 0)$, $(1, -2)$, and $(-1, -4)$?

Problem 2 | **Got It?** | Using a Quadratic Model

Learning Animation

a. The parabolic path of a thrown ball can be modeled by the table. The top of a wall is at $(5, 6)$. Will the ball go over the wall? If not, will it hit the wall on the way up, or the way down?

x	y
1	3
2	5
3	6

b. What is a reasonable domain and range for the function that models the path of the ball?

TEKS Process Standard (1)(C)

 Problem 3 | **Got It?** | **Using Quadratic Regression**

Learning
Animation

The table shows a meteorologist's predicted temperatures for a summer day in Denver, Colorado. What is a quadratic model for these data? Predict the high temperature for the day. At what time does the high temperature occur?

Denver, CO

Time	Predicted Temperature (°F)
6 A.M.	63
9 A.M.	76
12 P.M.	86
3 P.M.	89
6 P.M.	85
9 P.M.	76

ELPS Review what you previously learned about finding linear regression models. What calculator keys did you use? Compare the process to finding quadratic regression models. What is the minimum number of points you need for a quadratic equation? What calculator keys will you use?

Lesson Check

Do you know HOW?

Math
Tools

Online
Practice

Virtual Nerd
Tutorials

1. Find a quadratic function that passes through the points $(1, 0)$, $(2, -3)$, and $(3, -10)$.

2. Find a quadratic model for the data. Use the model to predict the maximum height of the object.

Time (sec)	0	1	2
Height (ft)	4	84	132

3. Use quadratic regression to find a quadratic model for the data.

x	−2	−1	0	1	2
y	3.5	3.5	7.5	15.5	27.5

Lesson Check

Do you UNDERSTAND?

Math Tools

Online Practice

Virtual Nerd Tutorials

4. Explain Mathematical Ideas (1)(G) Explain how you can write the equation of a parabola in vertex form if you know the vertex and another point on the parabola.

5. Select Techniques to Solve Problems (1)(C) How do you know whether to perform a linear regression or a quadratic regression for a given set of data?

6. Evaluate Reasonableness (1)(B) Your classmate says he can write the equation of a quadratic function that passes through the points (3, 4), (5, 22), and (3, 0). Is he correct? Explain why you agree or disagree.

TEXAS Test Practice

Multiple Choice

For Exercises 1–5, choose the correct letter.

1. A baseball coach records the height at every second of a ball thrown in the air. Some of the data appear in the table below.

Time (s)	0	1	3
Height (ft)	0	64	96

Which equation is a quadratic model for the data?

A. $h = -16t^2 + 80t$ **C.** $h = -32t^2 + 80t$

B. $h = -48t^2 + 112t$ **D.** $h = -16t^2 + 64t$

2. Use the table in Exercise 1. What is the height of the ball at 2.5 s?

F. 80 ft   **G.** 88 ft   **H.** 100 ft   **J.** 112 ft

3. On the parabola $f(x)$ that passes through the points $(1, -2)$, $(4, 1)$, and $(5, -2)$, for which of the following x-values does $f(x)$ have a positive value?

A. $x = 1$ **B.** $x = 3$ **C.** $x = 5$ **D.** $x = 7$

4. Which parabola passes through the points in the table at the right?

F. $y = -x^2 - x + 2$ **H.** $y = 2x^2 - 4x - 4$

G. $y = \frac{1}{2}x^2 - \frac{5}{2}x - 1$ **J.** $y = x^2 - 3x - 2$

x	f(x)
−1	2
2	−4
4	2

5. Which of the following sets of values cannot be modeled with a quadratic function?

A. $(2, 3), (0, -1), (3, 2)$ **C.** $(2, -7), (-1, 5), (3, -11)$

B. $f(2) = 7, f(-1) = -2, f(0) = 3$ **D.** $f(2) = -6, f(0) = -2, f(-1) = 3$

Short Response

6. The accountant for a small company studied the amount spent on advertising and the company's profit for several years. He made the table below. What is a quadratic model for the data? Show your work.

Advertising (Hundreds of Dollars)	1	2	3
Profit (Dollars)	269	386	501

Lesson 5-3 | Modeling With Quadratic Functions

SOLVE IT!

Carefully graph $y = \frac{1}{4}x^2$ and the point $F(0, 1)$. For $i = 1, 2, 3, 4, 5$, pick points P_i (five in all) nicely spaced on the parabola. Measure FP_i in millimeters. Directly below P_i, mark a point that is FP_i units down from P_i.

Based on the plot of these five points, what is likely true about any point $P(x, y)$ of the parabola? Verify your conjecture.

Interactive
Exploration

Vocabulary
Online

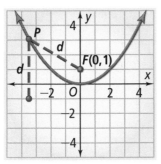

 Use Representations to Communicate Mathematical Ideas (1)(E) Describe how the representation you used to solve the problem successfully organizes and communicates your ideas.

Problem 1 | **Got It?** | Parabolas With Equation $y = ax^2$

Learning
Animation

a. What is an equation of the parabola with vertex $(0, 0)$ and focus $(0, -1.5)$?

b. What are the vertex, focus, and directrix of the parabola with equation $y = \frac{x^2}{4}$?

c. How does the distance of the focus from the vertex affect the shape of a parabola?

 Discuss the terms *vertex*, *focus* and *directrix* with a classmate. Draw a model parabola with labels for each term. Read the labels aloud. Then write a list of questions that will help you understand these terms. Find support from your teacher and peers to answer your questions.

 Problem 2 | **Got It?** | Parabolas With Equation $x = ay^2$

Learning
Animation

a. What is an equation of the parabola with vertex at the origin and directrix $x = -\frac{5}{2}$?

b. What are the vertex, focus, and directrix of the parabola with equation $x = -4y^2$?

TEKS Process Standard (1)(A)

Problem 3 | **Got It?** | Using Parabolas to Solve Problems

Learning Animation

The mirrored reflector of a flashlight is 8 cm across and 4 cm deep. How far from the vertex should the light bulb be positioned? (What is the focal length?)

TEKS Process Standard (1)(B)

Problem 4 | **Got It?** | Writing an Equation Given the Focus and the Directrix

Learning Animation

What is an equation of a parabola with focus $(0, 7)$ and directrix $y = -1$?

Problem 5 | **Got It?** | Writing an Equation of a Parabola

Learning Animation

What is an equation of the parabola with vertex $(1, 4)$ and focus $(1, 6)$?

Lesson Check

Do you know HOW?

Math
Tools

1. A parabola has vertex $(-2, 1)$ and focus $(-2, 0.5)$. Write the equation for the axis of symmetry and an equation for the parabola.

Online
Practice

Virtual Nerd
Tutorials

2. What is the equation of the parabola shown?

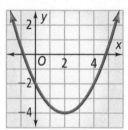

3. Identify the axis of symmetry, the focus, and the directrix of the parabola $y = (x + 2.5)^2 - 12.25$. Then sketch the graph of the parabola.

Lesson Check

Do you UNDERSTAND?

Math Tools

Online Practice

Virtual Nerd Tutorials

4. Vocabulary If the vertex of a parabola is 3 units from the focus, how far is the focus from the directrix?

5. Justify Mathematical Arguments (1)(G) The focus of the function $f(x)$ is on the line segment that joins the two points in the table. The function has a minimum at $(1, 0)$. What is the equation of the directrix? Justify your reasoning.

x	f(x)
−2	5
4	5

6. Explain Mathematical Ideas (1)(G) The vertex of a parabola is at the origin, one unit away from the focus. A student concludes that the equation is $y = \frac{1}{4}x^2$. Identify at least two ways that the student's equation might be in error.

TEXAS Test Practice

Multiple Choice

For Exercises 1–5, choose the correct letter.

1. The arch of this bridge is in the shape of the parabola $y = -\frac{1}{8}x^2 + 8$, where x and y are in feet. The horizontal walkway along the top of the bridge coincides with the directrix of the parabola. If you stand on the part of the walkway that is directly above the vertex of the arch, how many feet above the arch are you standing?

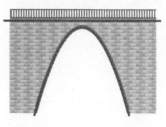

   A. 1   **B.** 2   **C.** 3   **D.** 4

2. A parabola has a directrix given by $y = a$ and a focus at $(0, -a)$, where a is a real number. Which of the following must be true?

   F. $a = 0$

   G. The vertex of this parabola is the origin.

   H. The equation of this parabola is $y = ax^2$.

   J. Such a parabola does not exist.

3. Which is the equation of a parabola with vertex at the origin and directrix $x = 2.5$?

   A. $x = -\frac{1}{10}y^2$ **B.** $x = \frac{1}{10}y^2$ **C.** $x = \frac{1}{2.5}y^2$ **D.** $x = -\frac{5}{2}y^2$

4. What is the directrix of $x = 2.25y^2$?

   F. $x = \frac{1}{4}$ **G.** $x = -\frac{1}{4}$ **H.** $x = \frac{1}{9}$ **J.** $x = -\frac{1}{9}$

5. Two parabolas, $f(x)$ and $g(x)$, each have their vertex at the origin. The focus of $f(x)$ is $(0, 5)$ and the focus of $g(x)$ is $\left(0, \frac{1}{10}\right)$. Which of the following is true?

   A. $g(1) > f(1)$ **B.** $g(0) > f(0)$ **C.** $f(0) > g(0)$ **D.** $f(1) > g(1)$

Short Response

6. What are the vertex, focus, and directrix of the parabola with equation $y = (x - 7)^2 - 44$? Show your work.

Lesson 5-4 | Focus and Directrix of a Parabola

SOLVE IT!

In a game, you see the two cards shown. You get two other cards with numbers. You win if

1. the product of your two numbers equals the number on one card shown, AND

2. the sum of your two numbers equals the number on the other card shown.

What should your two cards be for you to win the game? Is there more than one answer? Explain.

Interactive Exploration

Vocabulary Online

Use a Problem-Solving Model (1)(B) Evaluate your problem-solving model. Which parts were helpful? Which would you want to revise? Explain.

Problem 1 | **Got It?** | Factoring $ax^2 + bx + c$ when $a = \pm 1$

 Learning Animation

What is the expression in factored form?

  a. $x^2 + 14x + 40$

  b. $x^2 - 11x + 30$

  c. $-x^2 + 14x + 32$

 Problem 2 | **Got It?** | Finding Common Factors

 Learning Animation

What is the expression in factored form?

  a. $7n^2 - 21$

  b. $9x^2 + 9x - 18$

  c. $4x^2 + 8x + 12$

 Discuss factoring with a classmate. To learn how to factor quadratic expressions, ask questions such as: What properties should I know for factoring? How can I tell when a quadratic expression can't be factored?

Problem 3 **Got It?** Factoring $ax^2 + bx + c$ when $|a| \neq 1$

Learning
Animation

What is the expression in factored form? Check your answers.

a. $4x^2 + 7x + 3$ **b.** $2x^2 - 7x + 6$

c. Can you factor the expression $2x^2 + 2x + 2$ into a product of two binomials? Explain your answer.

TEKS Process Standard (1)(C)

 Problem 4 **Got It?** Factoring a Perfect Square Trinomial

Learning
Animation

What is $64x^2 - 16x + 1$ in factored form?

 Problem 5 **Got It?** Factoring a Difference of Two Squares

Learning
Animation

What is $16x^2 - 81$ in factored form?

Lesson 5-5 | Factoring Quadratic Expressions

145

Lesson Check

Do you know HOW?

Math
Tools

Online
Practice

Virtual Nerd
Tutorials

1. Factor the expressions and identify the method you used for each one.

   a. $25y^2 - 36$

   b. $x^2 - 13x + 12$

   c. $x^2 - 6x + 9$

2. Can the expression $m^2 + 4m + 6$ be factored into a product of two binomials? If so, write the factorization. If not, explain why not.

3. A designer makes a rectangular logo so that the length of the logo is twice the width x, in inches. Then she decides to enlarge the logo so that its area will be $2x^2 + 9x + 10$ square inches. By how many inches does she increase the length and width of the original logo? Assume all measurements are in whole numbers of inches.

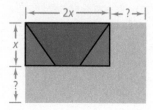

Do you UNDERSTAND?

4. Vocabulary Is $4b^2 - 26b + 169$ a perfect square trinomial? Explain.

Math
Tools

Online
Practice

Virtual Nerd
Tutorials

5. Analyze Mathematical Relationships (1)(F) How is factoring a trinomial $ax^2 + bx + c$ when $a \neq 1$ different from factoring a trinomial when $a = 1$? How is it similar?

6. Explain Mathematical Ideas (1)(G) Explain how to rewrite the expression $a^2 - 2ab + b^2 - 25$ as the product of two trinomial factors. (*Hint:* Group the first three terms. What type of expression is this?)

TEXAS Test Practice

Multiple Choice

For Exercises 1–5, choose the correct letter.

1. The area in square feet of a rectangular field is $2x^2 + x - 15$. If the length of the field, in feet, is $x + 3$ what is the width in terms of x?

   A. $2x + 3$ **B.** $2x - 5$ **C.** $2x - 3$ **D.** $2x + 5$

2. What is the complete factorization of $-x^2 + 3x + 28$?

   F. $(x - 4)(x - 7)$ **H.** $-(x + 4)(x + 7)$

   G. $-(x - 4)(x + 7)$ **J.** $-(x - 7)(x + 4)$

3. What is the complete factorization of $6x^2 + 9x - 6$?

   A. $3(2x - 1)(x + 2)$ **C.** $3(x - 2)(2x + 1)$

   B. $(3x + 2)(2x - 3)$ **D.** $3(x - 2)(2x - 1)$

4. What is the complete factorization of $a^2 - 2ab + b^2$?

   F. $(a - b)(a + b)$ **H.** $(a + b)(-a - b)$

   G. $(a + b)(a + b)$ **J.** $(a - b)(a - b)$

5. Which of the following is a perfect square trinomial?

   A. $x^2 + 9x + 18$ **C.** $3x^2 + 10x + 3$

   B. $x^2 + 6x + 9$ **D.** $x^2 - 4$

Short Response

6. The area in square meters of a rectangular parking lot is $x^2 - 95x + 2100$. The width in meters is $x - 60$. What is the length of the parking lot in meters? Show your work.

Lesson 5-5 | Factoring Quadratic Expressions

As part of an engineering project, your team is drawing a highway tunnel on a coordinate system. The tunnel opening is in the shape of a parabola. You need to finish the drawing. What are the coordinates of point C? Explain your reasoning.

Interactive Exploration

Vocabulary Online

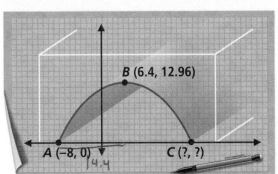

A (−8, 0)   B (6.4, 12.96)   C (?, ?)   14.4

14.4
+6.4
———
20.8

C (20.8, 0)

Evaluate Reasonableness (1)(B) Explain how you know your solution is reasonable.

The B is the vertex & the Axis of symmetry, so to calculate C's x-coordinates you add 14.4 to B's x-intercept & gain C's. Then since C's y-intercept is on 0, the y=0.

TEKS Process Standard (1)(E)

 Problem 1   **Got It?**   Solving a Quadratic Equation by Factoring

What are the solutions of the quadratic equation $x^2 - 7x = -12$?

Learning Animation

TEKS Process Standard (1)(C)

 Problem 2   **Got It?**   Solving a Quadratic Equation With Tables

What are the solutions of the quadratic equation $4x^2 - 14x + 7 = 4 - x$?

Learning Animation

 Problem 3   **Got It?**   Solving a Quadratic Equation by Graphing

What are the solutions of the quadratic equation $x^2 + 2x - 24 = 0$?

Learning Animation

Lesson 5-6 │ Quadratic Equations

Problem 4 | **Got It?** | Using a Quadratic Equation

Learning
Animation

a. The function $y = -0.03x^2 + 1.60x$ models the path of a kicked soccer ball. The height is y, the distance is x, and the units are meters. How far does the soccer ball travel? How high does the soccer ball go? Describe a reasonable domain and range for the function.

b. Are all domains and ranges reasonable for real-world situations? Explain.

ELPS After discussing the domain and range of a soccer ball with a partner, choose some other examples of projectile motion. Share your opinion on a reasonable domain and range for each.

Lesson Check

Do you know HOW?

1. Solve the equation $3x^2 - x - 2 = 0$ by factoring. Name the property that you used in your solution.

Math Tools

Online Practice

Virtual Nerd Tutorials

2. Write a quadratic function that has the zeros 2 and 7. Explain your method.

3. The function $y = -16x^2 + 64x$ models the height y, in feet, of a football that is kicked from the ground at time x, in seconds, after it is kicked. Does the football reach a height of 50 feet? If so, when? After how many seconds does the football land on the ground? Explain your answers.

Do you UNDERSTAND?

Math
Tools

Online
Practice

Virtual Nerd
Tutorials

4. **Vocabulary** If 5 is a zero of the function $y = x^2 + bx - 20$, what is the value of b? Explain.

5. **Select Techniques to Solve Problems (1)(C)** When is it easier to solve a quadratic equation by factoring than to solve it using a table?

6. **Analyze Mathematical Relationships (1)(F)** Using tables, how might you recognize that a quadratic equation likely has exactly one solution? No solution?

TEXAS Test Practice

Gridded Response

Solve each exercise and enter your answer in the grid provided.

1. The area encompassed by a square picture frame with side length x inches is given by x^2 in.^{2}. For a particular picture frame, the area encompassed can also be expressed as $2x + 35$ in.^{2}. What is the side length, in inches, of this picture frame? Solve by factoring.

2. What is the positive solution of the equation $4.5x^2 - 20 + x + 4 + x + 0.5x^2 = 0$? Solve by factoring.

3. What is the positive solution of the equation $x^2 - 3x = 1$? Solve by using a table or by graphing. If necessary, round your answer to the nearest hundredth.

4. What is the positive solution of the equation $3x^2 - 5x - 7 = 0$? Solve by using a table or by graphing. If necessary, round your answer to the nearest hundredth.

1. 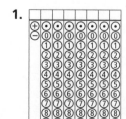   **2.** 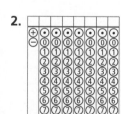   **3.** 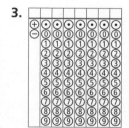   **4.**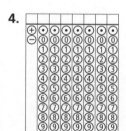

SOLVE IT!

How can you use pieces like these to form a square with side length $x + 3$ (and no overlapping pieces)? Show a sketch of your solution. How many of each piece do you need? Explain.

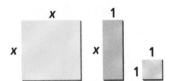

Interactive Exploration

Vocabulary Online

Connect Mathematical Ideas (1)(F) How does this problem relate to a problem you have seen before?

Problem 1 | **Got It?** | **Solving by Finding Square Roots**

What is the solution of each equation?

a. $7x^2 - 10 = 25$

b. $2x^2 + 9 = 13$

Learning
Animation

TEKS Process Standard (1)(A)

Problem 2 | **Got It?** | **Determining Dimensions**

The lengths of the sides of a rectangular window have the ratio 1.6 to 1. The area of the window is 2822.4 in.^{2}. What are the window dimensions?

Learning
Animation

Problem 3 **Got It?** Solving a Perfect Square Trinomial Equation

What is the solution of $x^2 - 14x + 49 = 25$?

Learning
Animation

TEKS Process Standard (1)(G)

 Problem 4 **Got It?** Completing the Square

a. What value completes the square for $x^2 + 6x$?

Learning
Animation

b. Is it possible for more than one value to complete the square for an expression? Explain.

ELPS Take turns explaining the new expression *completing the square*. Use a diagram to illustrate your description. Ask your classmate clarifying questions about what you heard.

Problem 5 | **Got It?** | **Solving by Completing the Square**

What is the solution of $2x^2 - x + 3 = x + 9$?

Learning Animation

TEKS Process Standard (1)(D)

 Problem 6 | **Got It?** | **Writing in Vertex Form**

What is $y = x^2 + 3x - 6$ in vertex form? Name the vertex, y-intercept, axis of symmetry, and direction of opening.

Learning Animation

Problem 7 | Got It? | Analyzing a Parabola

Learning
Animation

What are the vertex, focus, and directrix of the parabola with equation
$y = x^2 + 8x + 18$?

Lesson Check

Do you know HOW?

1. Solve the equation $(x - 3)^2 = 25$ by finding square roots.

Math
Tools

Online
Practice

Virtual Nerd
Tutorials

2. The equation $x^2 - 12x = 40 - k$ represents a parabola that intersects the x-axis at exactly one point. Find the value of k.

3. Wire fencing encloses a rectangular garden that is 16 feet longer than it is wide. By how much would the area of the garden increase if the same fencing were rearranged into a square?

Lesson Check

Do you UNDERSTAND?

4. Vocabulary Explain the process of completing the square.

Math Tools

Online Practice

Virtual Nerd Tutorials

5. Explain Mathematical Ideas (1)(G) How can you rewrite the equation $x^2 + 12x + 5 = 3$ so the left side of the equation is in the form $(x + a)^2$?

6. Evaluate Reasonableness (1)(B) Your friend completed the square and wrote the expression shown. Explain how you know your friend's result is unreasonable and then write the expression correctly.

$x^2 - 14x + 36$
$x^2 - 14x + 49 + 36$
$(x - 7)^2 + 36$

Multiple Choice

For Exercises 1–6, choose the correct letter.

1. The side length of a square window is x feet, and the window's area is $x + 3$ ft^2. What is the length of the window, in feet?

   A. $\sqrt{\frac{13}{4}} - \frac{1}{2}$ **B.** $\sqrt{\frac{13}{4}} + \frac{1}{2}$ **C.** $\sqrt{\frac{13}{2}} - \frac{1}{4}$ **D.** $\sqrt{\frac{13}{2}} + \frac{1}{4}$

2. What are the solutions of the equation $2x^2 + 16x + 28 = 0$?

   F. $-4 \pm \sqrt{30}$ **G.** $-4 \pm \sqrt{2}$ **H.** $4 \pm \sqrt{2}$ **J.** $4 \pm \sqrt{30}$

3. Which value completes the square for $x^2 - 3x$?

   A. $\frac{9}{4}$ **B.** $\frac{3}{2}$ **C.** 9   **D.** $-\frac{9}{4}$

4. Which value for k would make the left side of $x^2 + kx + \frac{49}{64} = 0$ a perfect square trinomial?

   F. 7   **G.** $\frac{7}{2}$ **H.** $\frac{7}{4}$ **J.** $\frac{7}{8}$

5. What are the solutions of the equation $x^2 = 8x - 1$?

   A. $-4 \pm \sqrt{17}$ **B.** $-4 \pm \sqrt{15}$ **C.** $4 \pm \sqrt{15}$ **D.** $4 \pm \sqrt{17}$

6. Which equation is the vertex form of $y = -3x^2 + 12x - 7$?

   F. $y = -3(x - 2)^2 - 5$ **H.** $y = -3(x + 2)^2 - 5$

   G. $y = -3(x - 2)^2 + 5$ **J.** $y = -3(x + 2)^2 + 5$

Short Response

7. The equation $p = -x^2 + 8x + 5$ gives the price p, in dollars, for a product when x million units are produced.

   a. What are the solutions of the equation $-x^2 + 8x + 5 = 0$?

   b. What is the positive solution to part (a) rounded to two decimal places? What does this solution mean in terms of this problem?

5-8 The Quadratic Formula

On this happy face, what quadratic function graphs a smile that

- crosses the *x*-axis twice?
- crosses the *x*-axis once?
- misses the *x*-axis completely?

Copy and show each completed face on graph paper. Explain why each mouth meets the given condition.

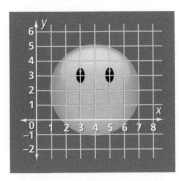

Interactive
Exploration

Vocabulary
Online

 Connect Mathematical Ideas (1)(F) What prior knowledge did you draw on to solve this problem?

Problem 1 **Got It?** **Using the Quadratic Formula**

What are the solutions? Use the Quadratic Formula.

a. $x^2 + 4x = -4$

 Learning Animation

b. $x^2 + 4x - 3 = 0$

TEKS Process Standard (1)(A)

 Problem 2 **Got It?** **Applying the Quadratic Formula**

a. Your school's jazz band is selling CDs at price x as a fundraiser. The total profit p is modeled by $p = -x^2 + 48x - 300$. What is the least amount, in dollars, that you can charge for a CD to make a $100 profit?

 Learning Animation

b. Would a negative profit make sense in this problem? Explain.

Problem 3 | **Got It?** | **Using the Discriminant**

What is the number of real solutions of each equation?

a. $2x^2 - 3x + 7 = 0$

b. $x^2 = 6x + 5$

ELPS Use what you heard in the lesson to answer the following: How many real solutions are possible for a quadratic equation? What formula can you use to find the discriminant? How does the discriminant relate to the number of real solutions for a quadratic equation?

Problem 4 | **Got It?** | **Using the Discriminant to Solve a Problem**

The height h of a golf ball at time t as it travels through the air is given by $h = -16t^2 + 85t + \frac{1}{12}$. Without solving an equation, will the golf ball reach a height of 110 ft? Explain.

Lesson Check

Do you know HOW?

Math Tools

Online Practice

Virtual Nerd Tutorials

1. Find the discriminant of $x^2 + 3x - 13 = 0$. Determine the number of real solutions. Then solve the equation using the Quadratic Formula.

2. For what values of k does the equation $x^2 + kx + 9 = 0$ have one real solution? Two real solutions?

3. The length of a rectangle is 5 centimeters greater than the width. The area of the rectangle is 47 square centimeters. What are the dimensions of the rectangle to the nearest tenth of a centimeter?

Lesson Check

Do you UNDERSTAND?

4. **Vocabulary** Explain how the discriminant is related to the definition of the word *discriminate*.

Math Tools

Online Practice

Virtual Nerd Tutorials

5. **Justify Mathematical Arguments (1)(G)** Your friend concluded that because two discriminants are equal, the solutions of the two equations are the same. Is your friend correct? If so, justify your friend's conclusion. If not, give an example of two quadratic equations that disprove this conclusion.

6. **Analyze Mathematical Relationships (1)(F)** If one quadratic equation has a positive discriminant, and another quadratic equation has a discriminant equal to 0, can the two quadratic equations share a solution? Explain why or why not. If so, give two quadratic equations that meet this criterion.

TEXAS Test Practice

Multiple Choice

For Exercises 1–6, choose the correct letter.

1. The function $3x^2 + 2x - 5$ models a company's profits as a function of the price x dollars (with $x > 0$) of the product the company sells. At what price, in dollars, will the company make zero profit? Use the Quadratic Formula.

    A. 1   **B.** $\frac{5}{3}$ **C.** 5   **D.** $\frac{1}{3}$

2. What is the solution of $2x^2 - 8x + 3 = 0$? Use the Quadratic Formula.

    F. $\frac{-4 \pm \sqrt{22}}{2}$ **G.** $\frac{-4 \pm \sqrt{10}}{2}$ **H.** $\frac{4 \pm \sqrt{10}}{2}$ **J.** $\frac{4 \pm \sqrt{22}}{2}$

3. What is the solution of $x^2 - 5x = 5$? Use the Quadratic Formula.

    A. $-5, 1$ **B.** $-1, 5$ **C.** $\frac{5 \pm \sqrt{5}}{2}$ **D.** $\frac{5 \pm 3\sqrt{5}}{2}$

4. Where does the parabola $y = x^2$ intersect with the line $y = 6x - 3$? Use the Quadratic Formula.

    F. $-3 \pm \sqrt{6}$ **G.** -3 **H.** 3   **J.** $3 \pm \sqrt{6}$

5. What is the discriminant of the equation $3x^2 - 7x + 1 = 0$?

    A. 61   **B.** 37   **C.** $\sqrt{37}$ **D.** -19

6. Which of the following can you conclude about the discriminant of the equation $ax^2 + \sqrt{ac}x + c = 0$, given that a and c are positive real numbers?

    F. It is positive.

    G. It is negative.

    H. It may be positive or negative, depending on the values of a and c.

    J. It is equal to zero.

Extended Response

7. The equation $d = n^2 - 12n + 43$ models the number of defective items d produced in a manufacturing process when there are n workers in a restricted area. Use the discriminant to answer the following questions. Show your work.

    a. Will the number of defective items ever be 10?

    b. Will the number of defective items ever be 7?

    c. Will the number of defective items ever be 5?

Lesson 5-8 | The Quadratic Formula

SOLVE IT!

Here is a partially-completed multiplication table. If you know that

$a \cdot a = a^2 = b,$

$a \cdot b = a \cdot a^2 = a^3 = c,$

$a^4 = d,$ and

$a^5 = a,$

how would you complete the table? What is a^{99}? Explain your reasoning.

Interactive
Exploration

Vocabulary
Online

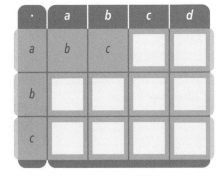

·	a	b	c	d
a	b	c		
b				
c				

Use Representations to Communicate Mathematical Ideas (1)(E) Describe how the representation you used to solve the problem successfully organizes and communicates your ideas.

Problem 1 | **Got It?** | Simplifying a Number Using i

How do you write each number by using the imaginary unit i?

a. $\sqrt{-12}$ **b.** $\sqrt{-25}$ **c.** $\sqrt{-7}$

d. Explain why $\sqrt{-64} \neq -\sqrt{64}$.

 Problem 2 | **Got It?** | Graphing in the Complex Number Plane

What are the graphs and absolute value of each number?

a. $5 - i$ **b.** $-3 - 2i$

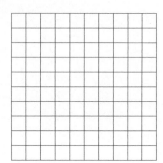 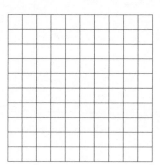

c. $1 + 4i$

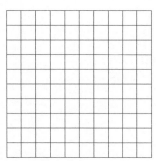

 With a classmate, design a Venn diagram showing the number systems you have already learned: natural, whole, integer, rational, irrational, and real. Extend the diagram to include the complex numbers. Trade with another pair and read their graphic organizer. Then read and solve the problem.

Lesson 5-9 | Complex Numbers

Problem 3 | Got It? | Adding and Subtracting Complex Numbers

Learning Animation

What is each sum or difference?

a. $(7 - 2i) + (-3 + i)$

b. $(1 + 5i) - (3 - 2i)$

c. $(8 + 6i) - (8 - 6i)$

d. $(-3 + 9i) + (3 + 9i)$

Problem 4 | Got It? | Multiplying Complex Numbers

Learning Animation

What is each product?

a. $(7i)(3i)$

b. $(2 - 3i)(4 + 5i)$

c. $(-4 + 5i)(-4 - 5i)$

Problem 5 | **Got It?** | **Dividing Complex Numbers**

Learning Animation

What is each quotient?

a. $\dfrac{5 - 2i}{3 + 4i}$

b. $\dfrac{4 - i}{6i}$

c. $\dfrac{8 - 7i}{8 + 7i}$

TEKS Process Standard (1)(F)

 Problem 6 | **Got It?** | Factoring Using Complex Conjugates

 Learning Animation

What are the factored forms of each expression?

a. $5x^2 + 20$

b. $x^2 + 81$

 Problem 7 | **Got It?** | Finding Imaginary Solutions

 Learning Animation

What are the solutions of each equation?

a. $3x^2 - x + 2 = 0$

b. $x^2 - 4x + 5 = 0$

Do you know HOW?

Math Tools

Online Practice

Virtual Nerd Tutorials

1. Simplify the expression $(4 - 2i) - (-3 + i)$. Then find the absolute value of the result.

2. Find the value of a: $(2 + i)(a - 5i) = 13 - 6i$

3. The figure shows the graph of the complex number $3 - 4i$. Plot and label five additional complex numbers that have the same absolute value as $3 - 4i$. Then state what you notice about the locations of all of the complex numbers you plotted.

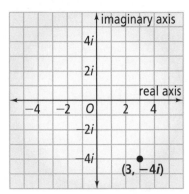

Do you UNDERSTAND?

Math Tools

Online Practice

Virtual Nerd Tutorials

4. Vocabulary Explain the difference between the additive inverse of a complex number and a complex conjugate.

5. Explain Mathematical Ideas (1)(G) Describe and correct the error made in simplifying the expression $(4 - 7i)(4 + 7i)$.

$(4 - 7i)(4 + 7i) = 16 + 28i - 28i + 49i^2$
$= 16 - 49$
$= -33$

6. Justify Mathematical Arguments (1)(G) A quadratic equation has real-number coefficients. Is it possible for the equation to have one real solution and one imaginary solution? Justify your response.

TEXAS Test Practice

Multiple Choice

For Exercises 1–8, choose the correct letter.

1. What is the length of the segment that has the origin as one endpoint and $(-7 + 5i) + (3 - 2i)$ as the other?

   A. $\sqrt{7}$ **B.** 5   **C.** 25   **D.** 36

2. The roots of a quadratic equation are given by $1 \pm \frac{\sqrt{-9}}{2}$. What is an equivalent expression for the roots?

   F. $1 \pm \frac{9i}{2}$ **G.** $1 \pm \frac{3i}{2}$ **H.** $2 \pm 3i$ **J.** $2 \pm 9i$

3. What is the simplified form of $(5 + \sqrt{-36}) - (-4 - \sqrt{-49})$?

   A. $9 - 13i$ **B.** $9 + 85i$ **C.** $1 - i$ **D.** $9 + 13i$

4. In the equation $\sqrt{10 - 3a} = b$, which of the following values for a will make b a pure imaginary number?

   F. -4 **G.** 0   **H.** $\frac{10}{3}$ **J.** 7

5. What is the simplified form of $(-3 + 2i)(1 - 4i)$?

   A. $-2 - 2i$ **B.** $-11 - 10i$ **C.** $5 + 14i$ **D.** $-3 - 8i$

6. What is the imaginary part of the number 9?

   F. i **G.** 0   **H.** $\sqrt{3}$ **J.** $3i$

7. What is $\frac{5 + 3i}{4 - 2i}$ written as a complex number?

   A. $\frac{7}{10} + \frac{11}{10}i$ **B.** $\frac{13}{10} + \frac{1}{10}i$ **C.** $\frac{5}{4} - \frac{3}{2}i$ **D.** $\frac{7}{10} - \frac{11}{10}i$

8. What is the factored form of the expression $4x^2 + 36$?

   F. $4(x + 3i)^2$ **H.** $4(x + 6i)^2$

   G. $4(x + 3i)(x - 3i)$ **J.** $4(x + 6i)(x - 6i)$

Short Response

9. What are the solutions of $2x^2 + 3x + 6 = 0$? Show your work.

A professional quarterback throws a football to a receiver. The ball follows the path shown in the graph. The receiver can catch the ball when it is between 3 ft and 7 ft from the ground. Approximately how far away should the receiver be from the quarterback in order to be able to catch the ball?

Interactive Exploration

Vocabulary Online

Path of Football Thrown

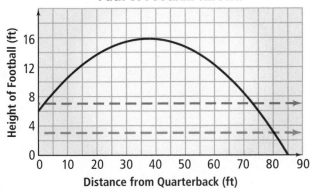

 Apply Mathematics (1)(A) Describe another real-world situation for which you could apply the same mathematical model.

Problem 1 | **Got It?** | Solving Inequalities Algebraically

Solve the inequality $4x^2 - 36x > 0$ algebraically.

Learning Animation

 Problem 2 | **Got It?** | Solving Inequalities Using a Table

Solve the inequality $x^2 + 3x - 4 > 0$ using a table.

Learning Animation

ELPS Read the Got It, and then discuss the following questions with a classmate. What does the shape of a parabola tell you about its y-values? Can you determine the vertex of the parabola by reading the values in the table? How can the values in the table help you determine which direction the parabola faces?

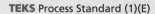

TEKS Process Standard (1)(E)

 Problem 3 | **Got It?** | Solving Inequalities Using a Graph

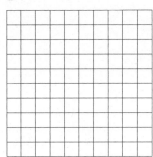

Find the solution sets for each inequality.

a. $\frac{1}{2}(x+4)^2 - 2 \le 0$

b. $\frac{1}{2}(x+4)^2 - 2 \ge 0$

Learning Animation

TEKS Process Standard (1)(A)

 Problem 4 | **Got It?** | Applying Quadratic Inequalities

A restaurant delivers meals to local businesses when they have evening meetings. The function $y = -5x^2 + 50x$ models the restaurant's profit y, in dollars, for an order of x meals. How many meals must be in an order for the restaurant to make a profit of at least \$105?

Learning Animation

Lesson Check

Do you know HOW?

1. Solve the inequalities $x^2 + 2x - 24 \leq 0$ and $x^2 + 2x - 24 \geq 0$. Which values, if any, are in both solution sets?

Math Tools

Online Practice

Virtual Nerd Tutorials

2. The solution of the inequality $x^2 + bx - 10 < 0$ is $-5 < x < 2$. What is the value of b?

3. A classmate chooses two secret numbers, x and y. You are told that $x + y = 15$ and $xy \geq 50$. Write and solve a quadratic inequality to find the range of possible values for x.

Do you UNDERSTAND?

Math Tools

Online Practice

Virtual Nerd Tutorials

4. **Connect Mathematical Ideas (1)(F)** How is solving a quadratic inequality similar to and different from solving a quadratic equation?

5. **Explain Mathematical Ideas (1)(G)** Is it possible for the solution of a quadratic inequality to be all real numbers? If so, give an example of such an inequality. If not, explain why not.

6. **Analyze Mathematical Relationships (1)(F)** How is the solution set of the inequality $ax^2 + bx + c < 0$ related to the solution set of the inequality $ax^2 + bx + c \geq 0$?

Lesson 5-10 | Quadratic Inequalities

181

Multiple Choice

For Exercises 1–5, choose the correct letter.

1. During the opening of a video game, the sun follows a path modeled by the function $y = -x^2 + 6x$, where y is the height of the sun above the horizon in centimeters and x is the time in minutes. For which times is the sun more than 8 centimeters above the horizon?

   A. $0 < x < 1$ or $x > 5$ **C.** $0 < x < 2$ or $x > 4$

   B. $1 < x < 5$ **D.** $2 < x < 4$

2. Which value is not in the solution set of the inequality $x^2 + 12x - 45 \geq 0$?

   F. -17 **G.** -14 **H.** 13 **J.** 15

3. Which of the following is a true statement about the inequality $\frac{1}{2}(x - 4)^2 - 1 \geq 0$?

   A. The graph of the solution set consists of two rays.

   B. The solution set is all real numbers.

   C. The inequality has no real solutions.

   D. The solution set has the form $a < x < b$ for some real numbers a and b.

4. How many integers are solutions of the inequality $x^2 + 5x \leq 14$?

   F. 8   **H.** 10

   G. 9   **J.** infinitely many

5. Given that k is a positive real number, which inequality has the solution set $0 < x < k$?

   A. $x^2 + kx < 0$ **B.** $x^2 + kx > 0$ **C.** $x^2 - kx < 0$ **D.** $x^2 - kx > 0$

Extended Response

6. Solve $(x + 3)^2 - 4 < 0$ by using a graph. Explain your method.

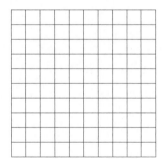

SOLVE IT!

In the Lesson 5-8 Solve It, you put a mouth on this face. What second quadratic function would you graph to open the mouth? Show the completed face.

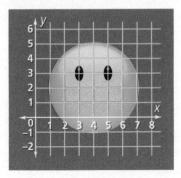

Interactive Exploration

Vocabulary Online

Connect Mathematical Ideas (1)(F) How does this problem relate to a problem you have seen before?

Problem 1 **Got It?** **Solving a Linear-Quadratic System by Graphing**

What is the solution of the system? $\begin{cases} y = x^2 + 6x + 9 \\ y = x + 3 \end{cases}$

Learning Animation

ELPS Discuss with a classmate. How was solving systems with two linear equations similar to solving a system with one quadratic and one linear equation? What are the possible solutions for this type of system? What do the graphs for each type of solution look like?

Problem 2 **Got It?** **Solving a Linear-Quadratic System Using Substitution**

What is the solution of the system? $\begin{cases} y = -x^2 - 3x + 10 \\ y = x + 5 \end{cases}$

Learning Animation

Lesson 5-11 | Systems of Linear and Quadratic Equations

Problem 3 **Got It?** Solving a Quadratic System of Equations

Learning
Animation

What is the solution of each system of equations?

a. $\begin{cases} y = x^2 - 4x + 5 \\ y = -x^2 + 5 \end{cases}$

b. $\begin{cases} y = x^2 - 4x + 5 \\ y = -x^2 - 5 \end{cases}$

 Problem 4 **Got It?** Formulating a Linear-Quadratic System

Learning
Animation

A Foucault pendulum traces a circle at its base with center (0, 0) and radius 10 units. Where does the pendulum intersect the edge of the base when its path (which must pass through the origin) has slope $-\frac{4}{3}$?

Do you know HOW?

Math Tools

Online Practice

Virtual Nerd Tutorials

1. What is the solution of the system of equations?

$$\begin{cases} y = x^2 - 3x - 3 \\ y = -2x^2 - x + 5 \end{cases}$$

2. Given that the following system has exactly one solution, what is the value of k? What is the solution of the system?

$$\begin{cases} y = x^2 - 3x + k \\ y = x - 2 \end{cases}$$

3. The coordinate plane, with $-5 \le x \le 5$ and $-5 \le y \le 5$, models a square reflecting pool. The path of a remote-control boat on the pool is modeled by the function $y = x^2 + 2x - 1$. The path of a second remote-control boat is a straight line through $(-2, 1)$ and $(3, -4)$. Find all points at which the two boats may collide.

Lesson 5-11 │ **Systems of Linear and Quadratic Equations**

186

Lesson Check

Do you UNDERSTAND?

Math Tools

Online Practice

Virtual Nerd Tutorials

4. Vocabulary How is a linear-quadratic system similar to and different from a system of two linear equations?

5. Evaluate Reasonableness (1)(B) A classmate solved the system shown below. He claims the solution is $(3.1, 5.7)$ and $(-2.8, 9.2)$. How can thinking about the graphs of these equations help you conclude that the solution is not reasonable?

$$\begin{cases} y = (x-1)^2 + 1 \\ y = -x^2 - 2 \end{cases}$$

6. Create Representations to Communicate Mathematical Ideas (1)(E) How many points of intersection can graphs of the following types of functions have? Draw graphs to justify your answers.

a. a linear function and a quadratic function

b. two quadratic functions

c. a quadratic function and an absolute value function (*Hint*: Graph $y = x^2$ and $y = |x|$ together. Can you transform one of the graphs slightly to increase the number of intersections?)

TEXAS Test Practice

Multiple Choice

For Exercises 1–4, choose the correct letter.

1. A child stands at the foot of a tall slide and throws a ball toward the top of the slide. The foot of the slide is located at the origin, the shape of the slide is modeled by the equation $y = 2x$, and the path of the ball through the air is modeled by $y = -x^2 + 5x$, where x is horizontal distance and y is vertical distance, both in feet. When the ball hits the slide, how many feet off the ground will it be?

   A. 5 feet   **B.** 6 feet   **C.** 7 feet   **D.** 8 feet

2. For which of the following values of c will the system $\begin{cases} y = -x^2 + 1 \\ y = x + c \end{cases}$ have two solutions?

   F. 1   **G.** 3   **H.** 5   **J.** 7

3. What is the solution of the system? $\begin{cases} y = x^2 - 4x + 3 \\ y = -2x + 6 \end{cases}$

   A. $(-1, 8), (3, 0)$ **C.** $(-1, 8), (4, 3)$

   B. $(-2, 10), (3, 0)$ **D.** $(0, 3), (4, -2)$

4. A system is given by $\begin{cases} y = x^2 + a \\ y = x + b \end{cases}$, where a and b may be any real numbers. Which of the following is true about the intersection of the graphs of the functions in the system?

   F. It is not possible for the graphs to intersect.

   G. The graphs will always intersect at only one point.

   H. It is not possible for the graphs to intersect at two points.

   J. It is possible that the graphs may intersect at two points.

Short Response

5. What is the solution to the system? Solve by graphing. $\begin{cases} y = -x^2 + 3x \\ y = x - 3 \end{cases}$

Lesson 5-11 | **Systems of Linear and Quadratic Equations**

SOLVE IT!

You are to move the stack of 5 rings to another post. Here are the rules.

- A move consists of taking the top ring from one post and placing it onto another post.
- You can only move one ring at a time.
- Do not place a ring on top of a smaller ring.

What is the fewest number of moves needed? How many moves are needed for 10 rings? 20 rings? Explain.

Interactive Exploration

Vocabulary Online

Use a Problem-Solving Model (1)(B) Evaluate your problem-solving model. Which parts were helpful? Which would you want to revise? Explain.

Problem 1 | **Got It?** | Comparing the Graphs of $y = 2^x$ and $y = 10^x$

Do the graphs of $y = 2^x$ and $y = 10^x$ intersect? How many times? Explain.

Learning
Animation

 Problem 2 | **Got It?** | Analyzing Attributes of the Graphs of $y = 2^x$ and $y = 10^x$

Find the maximum and minimum of $f(x) = 2^x$ on each interval.

a. $[-4, -1]$

b. $[-5, 3]$

c. $[-6, 0]$

Learning
Animation

Lesson 7-1 | Attributes of Exponential Functions

TEKS Process Standard (1)(A)

 Problem 3 **Got It?** **Identifying Exponential Growth and Decay**

Identify each function or situation as an example of exponential growth or decay. What is the *y*-intercept?

a. $y = 3\left(4^x\right)$

b. $y = 11\left(0.75^x\right)$

c. You put $2000 into a college savings account for four years. The account pays 6% interest annually.

ELPS Read and discuss the instructions with a classmate. How do the graphs of *exponential* growth and decay compare to the graphs of *linear* growth and decay? Can you explain the effects that *a* and *b* have on the graph of $y = ab^x$? What values of *b* indicate growth?

Lesson 7-1 | **Attributes of Exponential Functions**

221

TEKS Process Standard (1)(A)

 Problem 4 | **Got It?** | Modeling Exponential Growth

Suppose you invest $500 in a savings account that pays 3.5% annual interest. How much will be in the account after five years?

Learning
Animation

TEKS Process Standard (1)(E)

 Problem 5 | **Got It?** | Using Exponential Growth

a. Suppose you invest $500 in a savings account that pays 3.5% annual interest. If you make no additional deposits or withdrawals, when will the account contain at least $650?

Learning
Animation

b. Use the table below to determine when the account from Problem 5 will contain at least $1650. Explain.

X	Y1
4	1215.5
5	1276.3
6	1340.1
7	1407.1
8	1477.5
9	1551.3
10	1628.9

Y1 = 1551.32821598

Problem 6 | Got It? | **Writing an Exponential Function**

a. In Problem 6, you modeled the world population of Iberian lynx with the function $y = 150(0.8)^x$, where x is the number of years since 2003 and y is the population of lynx. What will be the world population of Iberian lynx in 2020?

Learning
Animation

b. If you graphed the model in part (a), would it ever cross the x-axis? Explain.

Lesson 7-1 | **Attributes of Exponential Functions**

223

Do you know HOW?

1. Without graphing, determine whether each function represents exponential growth or decay. Then state the domain and range of each function, and describe any asymptotes and intercepts.

   a. $f(x) = 10(0.45)^x$

   b. $g(x) = 3^x$

2. The maximum value of the function $f(x) = 2^x$ on an interval is 64. What is the maximum value of $g(x) = 10^x$ on the interval?

3. The table shows the number of subscribers to an online magazine in 2010 and 2011. If this trend continues and the number of subscribers is increasing exponentially, about how many new subscribers will the magazine gain between 2016 and 2017?

Year	Subscribers
2010	12,000
2011	12,720

Math Tools

Online Practice

Virtual Nerd Tutorials

Lesson 7-1 | **Attributes of Exponential Functions**

224

Lesson Check

Do you UNDERSTAND?

4. Vocabulary Explain how you can tell whether $y = ab^x$ represents exponential growth or decay.

Math Tools

Online Practice

Virtual Nerd Tutorials

5. Explain Mathematical Ideas (1)(G) A classmate says that the growth factor of the exponential function $y = 15(0.3)^x$ is 0.3. Is your classmate correct? If not, explain the error.

6. Analyze Mathematical Relationships (1)(F) Consider the exponential functions $y = 567^x$ and $y = 0.0284^x$. Using technology, explain how you know there is no point of intersection besides $(0,1)$.

Lesson 7-1 │ **Attributes of Exponential Functions**

Multiple Choice

For Exercises 1 and 2, choose the correct letter.

1. Suppose you deposit $3000 in a savings account that pays interest at an annual rate of 4%. If no other money is added or withdrawn from the account, how much will be in the account after 10 years?

   A. $3122.18   **C.** $4440.73

   B. $4994.50   **D.** $86,776.40

2. Which of the following functions represents exponential decay and has a y-intercept of 2?

   F. $y = 2\left(\frac{4}{3}\right)^x$ **H.** $y = \frac{1}{4}(2)^x$

   G. $y = \frac{1}{2}(0.95)^x$ **J.** $y = 2\left(\frac{2}{5}\right)^x$

Extended Response

3. In 2009 there was an endangered population of 270 cranes in a western state. Due to wildlife efforts, the population is increasing at a rate of 5% per year.

   a. What exponential function would be a good model for this population of cranes? Explain in words or show work for how you determined the exponential function.

   b. If this trend continues, how many cranes will there be in this population in 2020? Show your work.

f and g are exponential functions with the same base. Is the graph of g a *compression*, a *reflection*, or a *translation* of the graph of f? Or is it none of the above? Justify your reasoning.

Interactive Exploration

Vocabulary Online

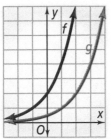

Connect Mathematical Ideas (1)(F) How does this problem relate to a problem you have seen before?

TEKS Process Standard (1)(D)

 Problem 1 **Got It?** Analyzing $y = af(x)$ for $f(x) = 2^x$

Graph each function on the same set of axes as the parent function $f(x) = 2^x$.

Learning Animation

a. $y = 0.5 \cdot 2^x$

b. $y = -4 \cdot 2^x$

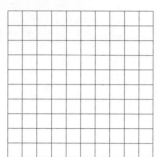

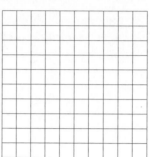

ELPS Discuss what you already know about stretching, compressing, and reflecting graphs with a classmate. What transformative effect does a in $y = ab^x$ have on the parent graph $y = b^x$? Work together to create a model showing the effects of each case: $a < -1$, $-1 < a < 0$, $0 < a < 1$, and $a > 1$.

TEKS Process Standard (1)(D)

 Problem 2 **Got It?** Analyzing $y = af(x)$ for $f(x) = 10^x$

Graph each function on the same set of axes as the parent function $f(x) = 10^x$. What is the effect of each transformation on the range?

Learning Animation

a. $y = \frac{1}{10} \cdot 10^x$

b. $y = -10^x$

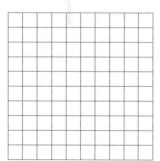

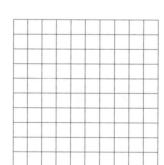

Lesson 7-2 | Transformations of Exponential Functions

Problem 3 **Got It?** Analyzing $y = f(x) + d$ for $f(x) = 2^x$

Graph each function on the same set of axes as the parent function $f(x) = 2^x$.
What is the effect of each transformation on the y-intercept?

 Learning Animation

a. $y = 2^x - 5$

b. $y = 2^x + 1$

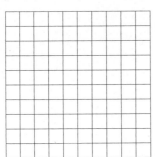

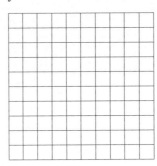

TEKS Process Standard (1)(D)

 Problem 4 **Got It?** Analyzing $y = f(x) + d$ for $f(x) = 10^x$

Graph each function on the same set of axes as the parent function $f(x) = 10^x$.
What is the effect of each transformation on the asymptote?

 Learning Animation

a. $y = 10^x - 10$

b. $y = 10^x + 50$

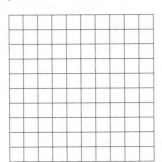

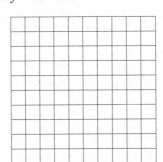

Lesson 7-2 | **Transformations of Exponential Functions**

Problem 5 | **Got It?** | Analyzing $y = f(x - c)$ for $f(x) = 2^x$

Graph each function on the same set of axes as the parent function $f(x) = 2^x$. What is the effect of each transformation on the domain?

Learning Animation

a. $y = 2^{(x+3)}$

b. $y = 2^{(x-6)}$

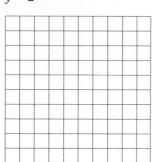

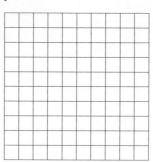

 Problem 6 | **Got It?** | Analyzing $y = f(x - c)$ for $f(x) = 10^x$

Graph each function on the same set of axes as the parent function $f(x) = 10^x$. What is the effect of each transformation on the asymptote?

Learning Animation

a. $y = 10^{(x-1)}$

b. $y = 10^{(x+4)}$

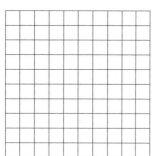

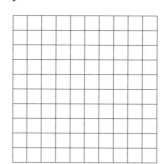

Lesson 7-2 | Transformations of Exponential Functions

230

Problem 7 | Got It? | **Using an Exponential Model**

Learning
Animation

a. The best temperature to brew coffee is between 195°F and 205°F. The table shows temperature readings from a sample cup of coffee. How long does it take for the coffee to reach a temperature of 100 degrees? Use an exponential model.

Time (min)	Temp (°F)
0	203
5	177
10	153
15	137
20	121
25	111
30	104

b. In Problem 7, would the model of the exponential data be useful if you did not translate the data by 68 units? Explain.

Lesson 7-2 | **Transformations of Exponential Functions**

231

Lesson Check

Do you know HOW?

Math Tools

Online Practice

Virtual Nerd Tutorials

1. Graph the function $y = 2^{(x-1.5)}$ on the same set of axes as the parent function. Then use transformations to describe how the two graphs are related.

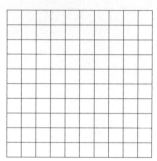

2. Write a function rule in the form $y = 10^{(x-c)} + d$ for the function shown in the graph.

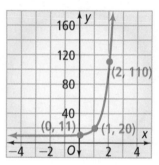

3. The table shows the temperature of a cup of coffee as it cools. Given a room temperature of 71°F, how long does it take the coffee to cool from 100°F to 90°F? Use an exponential model and round to the nearest minute.

Time (min)	Temp (°F)
0	186
2	175
8	156
18	135
28	120

Lesson Check

Do you UNDERSTAND?

4. **Vocabulary** Why are there multiple exponential parent functions rather than a single exponential parent function?

5. **Explain Mathematical Ideas (1)(G)** A classmate was asked to graph $y = 2^x - 2$ and $y = 2^x - 3$. After making the graphs, your classmate says that the two graphs intersect. Do you think your classmate is correct? Explain.

6. **Analyze Mathematical Relationships (1)(F)** Write three different exponential functions that have the parent function $y = 10^x$ and whose graphs pass through the point $(0, 2)$.

TEXAS Test Practice

Multiple Choice

For Exercises 1–5, choose the correct letter.

1. The function $y = 2^x + 3$ models the number of people y who watch an online video each month, where x is the number of months since the video was created. Which of the following is a true statement about the graph of the function?

   A. The graph is a vertical stretch of the graph of the parent function $y = 2^x$.

   B. The graph intersects the line $y = 3$.

   C. The y-intercept of the graph is $(0, 3)$.

   D. The graph intersects the line $x = 3$.

2. Which of the following functions has a graph that intersects the x-axis?

   F. $y = 10^x - 2$ **H.** $y = -10^x - 2$

   G. $y = 2 \cdot 10^x$ **J.** $y = 10^x + 2$

3. A student used software to graph the function $y = 2^x$. Then he used the software to reflect the graph in the x-axis and shift it 2 units right. Which function matches the resulting graph?

   A. $y = -2^x - 2$ **C.** $y = -2^{(x-2)}$

   B. $y = -2^x + 2$ **D.** $y = -2^{(x+2)}$

4. Which transformation can be applied to the graph of $y = 10^{(x-4)}$ to create the graph of $y = 10^{(x+3)}$?

   F. translation 7 units right   **H.** translation 7 units down

   G. translation 7 units left   **J.** translation 7 units up

5. Which function has a graph with an asymptote of the form $y = k$, where $k < 0$?

   A. $y = -10^x - 5$ **C.** $y = -2^{(x-1)}$

   B. $y = 10^{(x-4)}$ **D.** $y = 2^x + 3$

Short Response

6. Graph the functions $y = 2^x$ and $y = -2 \cdot 2^x$ and use transformations to describe how the graphs are related.

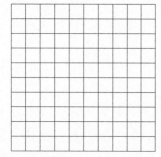

Lesson 7-2 | **Transformations of Exponential Functions**

234

SOLVE IT!

You have $1000 to invest. When you open an account, a special promotion allows you to choose from three options for dividing 6% interest over the first year. Which option would you choose? Explain.

Interactive Exploration

Vocabulary Online

Apply Mathematics (1)(A) Describe another real-world situation for which you could apply the same mathematical model.

Problem 1 | **Got It?** | Evaluating e^x

Learning
Animation

How can you use a graphing calculator to evaluate e^8?

ELPS Discuss the number e with a classmate. Why do you think this number is represented by a letter? Come up with two questions that help clarify what you heard in the lesson—one about the definition of e, and one about how to evaluate e^x.

TEKS Process Standard (1)(E)

 Problem 2 | **Got It?** | Analyzing the Attributes of $y = e^x$

Learning
Animation

How is the range of the function $y = e^x$ related to the shape of the function's graph?

Lesson 7-3 | Attributes and Transformations of $f(x) = e^x$

TEKS Process Standard (1)(D)

 Problem 3 **Got It?** Analyzing $y = af(x)$ for $f(x) = e^x$

Graph each function on the same set of axes as the parent function $f(x) = e^x$.
What is the effect of each transformation on the y-intercept?

a. $y = 2 \cdot e^x$

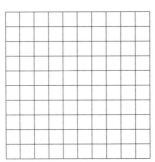

b. $y = -\frac{1}{3} \cdot e^x$

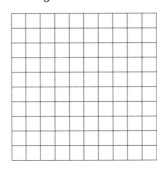

Lesson 7-3 │ Attributes and Transformations of $f(x) = e^x$

TEKS Process Standard (1)(D)

 Problem 4 | **Got It?** | Analyzing $y = f(x) + d$ for $f(x) = e^x$

Graph each function on the same set of axes as the parent function $f(x) = e^x$.
What is the effect of each transformation on the asymptote?

a. $y = e^x - 1$

b. $y = e^x + 4$

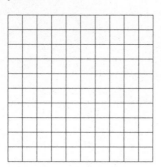
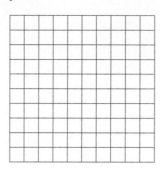

Learning Animation

 Problem 5 | **Got It?** | Analyzing $y = f(x - c)$ for $f(x) = e^x$

Graph each function on the same set of axes as the parent function $f(x) = e^x$.
What is the effect of each transformation on the domain?

a. $y = e^{(x-2)}$

b. $y = e^{(x+8)}$

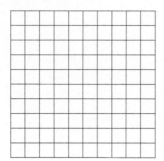
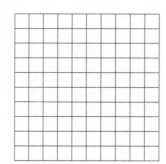

Learning Animation

Lesson 7-3 | Attributes and Transformations of $f(x) = e^x$

Problem 6 | **Got It?** | **Continuously Compounded Interest**

Learning
Animation

Suppose you won a contest at the start of 5th grade that deposited $3000 in an account that pays 5% annual interest compounded continuously. To the nearest dollar, how much will be in the account after 8 years?

Lesson Check

Do you know HOW?

1. Graph the function $y = e^x - \frac{1}{2}$ on the same set of axes as the parent function. Then analyze the domain, range, and asymptotes of $y = e^x - \frac{1}{2}$.

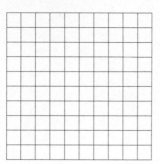

2. The graph of $g(x)$ is a vertical compression of the graph of the parent function $f(x) = e^x$ by a factor of 0.5 followed a translation 2 units left. Graph $g(x)$ and write a rule for $g(x)$.

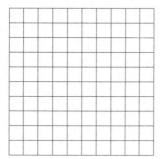

3. Five years ago, you invested some money in a savings account that pays 2% annual interest compounded continuously. Today, the value of the money in the account is $574.69. How much money did you invest in the account five years ago?

Lesson Check

Do you UNDERSTAND?

4. **Vocabulary** How is a natural base exponential function similar to an exponential function with the base 2?

Math Tools

Online Practice

Virtual Nerd Tutorials

5. **Evaluate Reasonableness (1)(B)** A student said that the maximum value of the function $y = e^x$ on the interval $[1, 3]$ is approximately 30.1. You do not have a calculator to check her work. Explain how you can use estimation to decide if her answer is reasonable.

6. **Analyze Mathematical Relationships (1)(F)** Is investing $2000 in an account that pays 5% annual interest compounded continuously the same as investing $1000 at 4% and $1000 at 6%, each compounded continuously? Explain your answer.

TEXAS Test Practice

Multiple Choice

For Exercises 1–5, choose the correct letter.

1. A friend invests $320 in an account that pays 3% annual interest compounded continuously. Which is the best estimate of the amount of interest the account earns between the end of the 4th year and the end of the 5th year?

   A. $9   **B.** $11   **C.** $52   **D.** $61

2. Which pair of functions has the same asymptote?

   F. $y = e^{(x-9)}$ and $y = e^x - 9$ **H.** $y = e^x - 9$ and $y = -e^x - 9$

   G. $y = e^x - 9$ and $y = -e^x + 9$ **J.** $y = e^{(x+9)}$ and $y = e^x - 9$

3. Which function has a graph that intersects the graph of $y = e^x + 2$?

   A. $y = e^x - 2$ **C.** $y = -e^x + 2$

   B. $y = e^{(x-1)} + 2$ **D.** $y = e^{(x+2)}$

4. Given that $a > 0$, which of the following is a true statement about the function $y = ae^x$?

   F. The graph of the function is a translation of the graph of $y = e^x$.

   G. The maximum value of the function on the interval $[0, 1]$ occurs at $x = 1$.

   H. The range of the function is $y > a$.

   J. The function has exactly one x-intercept.

5. Which function does not have the value $y = 6$ in its range?

   A. $y = 6e^x$ **C.** $y = e^x - 6$

   B. $y = e^{(x-6)}$ **D.** $y = e^x + 6$

Short Response

6. The graph of $f(x) = 2e^x + 1$ is reflected in the x-axis to make the graph of $g(x)$. Write a function rule for $g(x)$ and draw its graph.

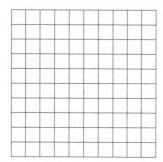

SOLVE IT!

For each figure, how is the number on the center tile related to the numbers on the other tiles? What will be the center number in Figure 6? In Figure 10? In Figure n? Explain your reasoning.

Interactive Exploration

Vocabulary Online

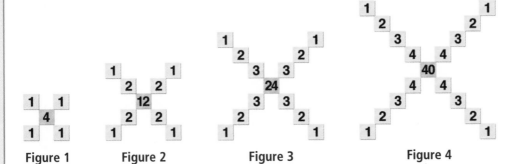

Figure 1   Figure 2   Figure 3   Figure 4

 Explain Mathematical Ideas (1)(G) A classmate questions your solution to the problem. Use precise mathematical language to explain why your solution is correct.

Problem 1 | **Got It?** | **Formulating Recursive Exponential Functions**

Learning
Animation

The table shows the number of visitors to a writer's blog over a period of several months. Write an explicit formula and a recursive formula to model the data.

Month	1	2	3	4	5
Visitors	9	36	144	576	2304

ELPS Discuss with a classmate. How do the everyday meanings of explicit and recursive help you to understand what you heard in the lesson? How is the domain of the function $y = b^x$ different from the domain of the explicit formula $a_n = b^n$?

Lesson 7-4 | Exponential Models in Recursive Form

Problem 2 | Got It? | Writing Exponential Functions in Recursive Form

Learning Animation

The function $y = 8 \cdot 2^x$ models the number of *E. coli* cells y in a petri dish x hours after the start of an experiment. If you want to know the number of cells in the petri dish after 15 hours, is it easier to use the given equation or a recursive formula? Explain.

TEKS Process Standard (1)(A)

Problem 3 | Got It? | Using a Recursive Exponential Function to Model a Situation

Learning Animation

You invest $850 in a savings account that pays 3% annual interest. Write an explicit formula and a recursive formula to model the situation.

Lesson Check

Do you know HOW?

1. The table shows the number of page views for a new Web site over a period of several days. Write an explicit formula and a recursive formula to model the data. Then find the number of page views on Day 10.

Day	Page Views
1	3
2	6
3	12
4	24
5	48

Math Tools

Online Practice

Virtual Nerd Tutorials

2. The growth of an investment may be modeled by the explicit formula $a_n = P(1.03)^n$, where P is the initial amount invested, in dollars, and n is the number of years since the initial investment. Write a recursive formula to model the situation.

3. The table shows the value of a rare coin, which grows exponentially with time, over a period of several years. Some of the table is covered by drops of ink. Use an exponential model to write a recursive formula for the situation.

Year	Value ($)
1	
	1440.00
5	2073.60
6	2488.32

Lesson Check

Do you UNDERSTAND?

Math Tools

Online Practice

Virtual Nerd Tutorials

4. **Vocabulary** Is it easier to use an explicit formula or a recursive formula if you want to know the 20th term of a sequence? Why?

5. **Explain Mathematical Ideas (1)(G)** In a recursive formula, $a_1 > 0$ and $a_n = k \cdot a_{n-1}$, with $k > 0$. Explain how the value of k in the formula tells you whether the terms of the sequence are increasing or decreasing.

6. **Justify Mathematical Arguments (1)(G)** A classmate said that it is sometimes possible to write a recursive formula for an exponential model in which $a_1 = 0$. Do you agree? Justify your response.

TEXAS Test Practice

Multiple Choice

For Exercises 1–5, choose the correct letter.

1. The population of a town n years after 2000 is modeled by the recursive formula $a_1 = 32,000$ and $a_n = 0.95a_{n-1}$. Which of the following is a true statement about the situation?

   A. An explicit formula for the population of the town is $a_n = 32,000(0.95)^{n-1}$.

   B. The town's population increased by 95% each year.

   C. The population of the town in 2002 was 28,880.

   D. The population of the town increased or decreased by the same number of people each year.

2. Which recursive formula models the same sequence as the explicit formula $a_n = 2.5(3)^n$?

   F. $a_1 = 3$ and $a_n = 2.5a_{n-1}$ **H.** $a_1 = 7.5$ and $a_n = 3a_{n-1}$

   G. $a_1 = 2.5$ and $a_n = 3a_{n-1}$ **J.** $a_1 = 7.5$ and $a_n = 2.5a_{n-1}$

3. Which recursive formula models a sequence in which all terms are greater than 10?

   A. $a_1 = 12$ and $a_n = 0.9a_{n-1}$ **C.** $a_1 = 45$ and $a_n = a_{n-1} - 5$

   B. $a_1 = 60$ and $a_n = 0.5a_{n-1}$ **D.** $a_1 = 18$ and $a_n = 1.2a_{n-1}$

4. The number of cells in a test tube increases according to an exponential relationship. After 2 hours, there are 32 cells. After 4 hours, there are 128 cells. If a_n represents the number of cells in the test tube after n hours, which of the following recursive formulas models the situation?

   F. $a_1 = 8$ and $a_n = 2a_{n-1}$ **H.** $a_1 = 16$ and $a_n = 4a_{n-1}$

   G. $a_1 = 32$ and $a_n = 4a_{n-1}$ **J.** $a_1 = 4$ and $a_n = 2a_{n-1}$

5. A sequence is modeled by the recursive formula $a_1 = 3$ and $a_n = 5a_{n-1}$. What is the ratio of any term in the sequence to the term after it?

   A. 5   **B.** 3   **C.** $\frac{1}{3}$ **D.** $\frac{1}{5}$

Short Response

6. The table shows the total number of portable music players sold by a technology company. Write an explicit formula and a recursive formula to model the data.

Year	Number Sold (millions)
1	6
2	9
3	13.5
4	20.25
5	30.375

Lesson 7-4 | **Exponential Models in Recursive Form**

248

SOLVE IT!

The chart shows the different ways you can write 4 and 16 in the form a^b, where a and b are positive integers and $a \neq 1$. What is the smallest number you can write in this a^b form in four different ways? In five different ways? In seven different ways? Explain how you found your answers.

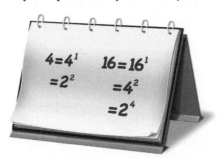

$$4 = 4^1 \qquad 16 = 16^1$$
$$= 2^2 \qquad\quad = 4^2$$
$$\qquad\qquad = 2^4$$

Interactive Exploration

Vocabulary Online

 Create Representations to Communicate Mathematical Ideas (1)(E)
Describe how the representation you made successfully organizes and communicates your solution to the problem.

Problem 1 | **Got It?** | **Writing Exponential Equations in Logarithmic Form**

Learning
Animation

What is the logarithmic form of each equation?

a. $36 = 6^2$

b. $\frac{8}{27} = \left(\frac{2}{3}\right)^3$

c. $1 = 3^0$

 Discuss with a classmate the new equation structure presented during classroom instruction. Work together to write the *logarithmic form* of each equation in the Got It. Listen to each other read the new equations, and help rephrase any statements that do not use terms in the correct order.

TEKS Process Standard (1)(F)

 Problem 2 | **Got It?** | **Evaluating a Logarithm**

Learning
Animation

What is the value of each logarithm?

a. $\log_5 125$

b. $\log_4 32$

c. $\log_{64} \frac{1}{32}$

Problem 3 | **Got It?** | **Graphing the Inverse of a Function**

The volume of a cloud of gas increases by a factor of 10 every hour. The function $g(x)$ represents the volume of the cloud after x hours. Find $g^{-1}(x)$ and describe what $g^{-1}(x)$ represents in this context.

Learning Animation

Problem 4 | **Got It?** | **Analyzing Attributes of Logarithmic Functions**

Use the graphs of $f(x) = \log_2 x$ and $g(x) = \log_{10} x$ in Problem 4 to determine whether $>$, $<$, or $=$ best completes each statement.

Learning Animation

a. $f(0.5)$ _____ $g(0.5)$

b. $f(1)$ _____ $g(1)$

c. $f(5)$ _____ $g(5)$

Problem 5 | **Got It?** | **Finding the Maximum and Minimum of Logarithmic Functions**

Use the graphs of $f(x) = \log_2 x$ and $g(x) = \log_{10} x$ to find the minimum and maximum values of the functions on the interval $[32, 100]$. If necessary, round to the nearest thousandth.

Learning Animation

Lesson 7-5 | Attributes of Logarithmic Functions

251

Lesson Check

Do you know HOW?

Math
Tools

Online
Practice

Virtual Nerd
Tutorials

1. Evaluate the logarithm $\log_2 \frac{1}{4}$. Use your answer to write an exponential equation and its corresponding logarithmic equation.

2. The minimum value of the function $f(x) = \log_2 x$ on an interval is 4. What is the approximate minimum value of $g(x) = \log_{10} x$ on the interval?

3. The function $f(x) = \log_2 x$ models the number of hours it takes for a single cell to repeatedly divide into two until there are x cells. A test tube currently contains 1024 cells. How long will it take until the test tube contains 8192 cells?

Lesson Check

Do you UNDERSTAND?

Math
Tools

Online
Practice

Virtual Nerd
Tutorials

4. **Vocabulary** Determine whether each logarithm is a common logarithm.

   a. $\log_2 4$

   b. $\log 64$

   c. $\log_{10} 100$

   d. $\log_5 5$

5. **Connect Mathematical Ideas (1)(F)** Explain how you could use the function $y = 6^x$ to graph the logarithmic function $y = \log_6 x$.

6. **Create Representations to Communicate Mathematical Ideas (1)(E)**
A student said that for all positive values of x, $x > \log x$. Do you agree?
Use a graph to explain your answer.

TEXAS Test Practice

Multiple Choice

For Exercises 1–4, choose the correct letter.

1. If $\log(4x) = 3$, what is x?

A. $\dfrac{\log 3}{4}$ **B.** $\dfrac{3}{4}$ **C.** 75   **D.** 1000

2. Which of the following is true about the graphs $f(x) = \log_2(x)$ and $g(x) = \log_{10}(x)$?

  F. $f(x)$ and $g(x)$ intersect the x-axis at the same point.

  G. $g(x) > f(x)$ for all x.

  H. $f(x)$ and $g(x)$ have different domains.

  J. $f(x)$ and $g(x)$ have different ranges.

3. Which of the following is the logarithmic form of the equation $4^{-3} = \frac{1}{64}$?

  A. $\log_{-3}\frac{1}{64} = 4$ **C.** $\log_4\frac{1}{64} = -3$

  B. $\log_{-3}4 = \frac{1}{64}$ **D.** $\log_{\frac{1}{64}}4 = -3$

4. What is the value of $\log_2 8$?

  F. 64   **G.** 8   **H.** 16   **J.** 3

Short Response

5. A single-celled bacterium divides every hour. The number N of bacteria after t hours is given by the formula $\log_2 N = t$.

  a. After how many hours will there be 64 bacteria?

  b. Explain in words or show work for how you determined the number of hours.

Lesson 7-5 │ **Attributes of Logarithmic Functions**

 SOLVE IT!

You are in the final round of a game of "Logarithm Scramble." The goal is to find cards that satisfy the equations shown. What are some possible combinations of cards?

In order to win the game, the rules state that the combinations must contain only cards with logarithmic expressions. What two combinations would you use to win the game? Explain your choices.

Interactive Exploration

Vocabulary Online

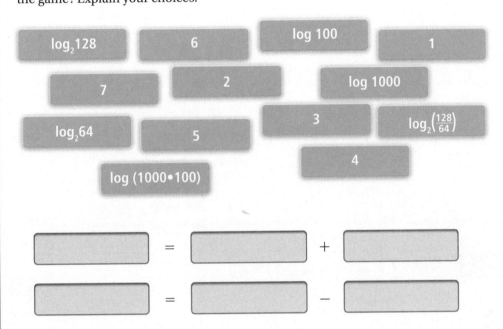

$\log_2 128$ 6   log 100   1

7   2   log 1000

$\log_2 64$ 5   3 $\log_2\left(\frac{128}{64}\right)$

log (1000•100)   4

[_____] = [_____] + [_____]

[_____] = [_____] − [_____]

 Analyze Mathematical Relationships (1)(F) What mathematical relationships did you identify in the problem? How did you use them to solve the problem?

Problem 1 | **Got It?** | **Simplifying Logarithms**

Learning Animation

What is each expression written as a single logarithm?

a. $\log_4 5x + \log_4 3x$

b. $2\log_4 6 - \log_4 9$

Problem 2 | **Got It?** | **Expanding Logarithms**

Learning Animation

What is each logarithm expanded?

a. $\log_3 \frac{250}{37}$

b. $\log_3 9x^5$

 Reread the lesson introduction and take notes that will help you expand logarithms. Discuss the properties of logarithms with a classmate. Explain the difference between *writing an expression as a single logarithm* and *expanding a logarithm*. Do you use the same formulas for solving both kinds of problems?

Problem 3 **Got It?** **Using the Change of Base Formula**

Use the Change of Base Formula. What is the value of each expression?

a. $\log_8 32$

b. $\log_4 18$

 Problem 4 **Got It?** **Using a Logarithmic Scale**

The pH of a substance equals $-\log[\text{H}^+]$, where $[\text{H}^+]$ is the concentration of hydrogen ions. Suppose the hydrogen ion concentration for Substance A is twice that for Substance B. Which substance has the greater pH level? What is the greater pH level minus the lesser pH level? Explain.

Lesson 7-6 | **Properties of Logarithms**

257

Lesson Check

Do you know HOW?

1. Write the expression $\log_4 2 + \log_4 9$ as a single logarithm. Then use the Change of Base Formula to find the value of the resulting expression.

Math
Tools

Online
Practice

Virtual Nerd
Tutorials

2. Use the fact that $\log_5 2 \approx 0.43$ and $\log_5 6 \approx 1.11$ to find the approximate value of $\log_5 72$ without using a calculator. Show your work.

3. The half-life of a radioactive isotope is the time it takes for half of the atoms in the material to disintegrate. For Sodium-24, the equation shown below relates the amount of material at the start A_0, the current amount of material A, and the time t that has elapsed in hours. Given that the starting amount was 24 mg and the current amount is 3 mg, find the time that has elapsed without using a calculator.

$$-\frac{t}{15} = \log_2 A - \log_2 A_0$$

Lesson Check

Do you UNDERSTAND?

Math
Tools

Online
Practice

Virtual Nerd
Tutorials

4. **Vocabulary** State which property or properties need to be used to write each expression as a single logarithm.

   a. $\log_4 5 + \log_4 5$

   b. $\log_5 4 - \log_5 6$

5. **Evaluate Reasonableness (1)(B)** A classmate said that the value of $\log_3 35$ is approximately 4.15. Without using a calculator, explain whether your classmate's answer is reasonable.

6. **Explain Mathematical Ideas (1)(G)** Given a number written in scientific notation, $a \times 10^n$, explain why you only need to know the value of $\log a$ in order to find the value of $\log(a \times 10^n)$.

Multiple Choice

For Exercises 1–5, choose the correct letter.

1. The difference d in decibels between two signals of intensity I_1 and I_2 can be calculated using the formula $d = 10 \log \frac{I_2}{I_1}$. Which of the following is an equivalent formula for d?

A. $d = \log(I_2)^{10} - \log I_1$

B. $d = \log(I_2)^{10} - \log(I_1)^{10}$

C. $d = 10 \log I_2 + \log I_1$

D. $d = \log(10 I_2) - \log I_1$

2. Which expression is the correct expansion of $\log_4(3x)^2$?

F. $\frac{1}{2}(\log_4 3 - \log_4 x)$

G. $2(\log_4 3 + \log_4 x)$

H. $2(\log_4 3 - \log_4 x)$

J. $2\log_4 3 + \log_4 x$

3. Which of the following expressions are equivalent?

I. $\frac{4\log 2}{\log 7}$

II. $\log_7 16$

III. $\frac{4\log_7 2}{\log 10}$

IV. $\log_7 8$

A. I and II

B. II and III

C. III and IV

D. I and IV

4. Which statement correctly expresses $4\log_3 x + 7\log_3 y$ as a single logarithm?

F. $\log_3 x^4 y^7$

G. $\log_3(4x + 7y)$

H. $\log_3(x^4 + y^7)$

J. $\log_3(4x - 7y)$

5. Which statement correctly demonstrates the Power Property of Logarithms?

A. $\frac{1}{2}\log_5 9 = \log_5 81$

B. $\frac{1}{2}\log_5 9 = \log_5 \frac{9}{2}$

C. $\frac{1}{2}\log_5 9 = \log_5 18$

D. $\frac{1}{2}\log_5 9 = \log_5 3$

Short Response

6. The pH of a substance equals $-\log[H^+]$, where $[H^+]$ is the concentration of hydrogen ions. The concentration of hydrogen ions in pure water is 10^{-7} and the concentration of hydrogen ions in a sodium hydroxide solution is 10^{-14}.

a. Without using a calculator, what is the difference of the pH levels of pure water and the sodium hydroxide solution?

b. Explain in words or show work for how you determined the difference of the pH levels.

SOLVE IT!

f and g are logarithmic functions with the same base. Is the graph of g a *compression*, a *reflection*, or a *translation* of the graph of f? Or is it a series of transformations? Justify your reasoning.

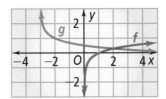

Interactive Exploration

Vocabulary Online

 Use Representations to Communicate Mathematical Ideas (1)(E)
Describe how the representation you used to solve the problem successfully organizes and communicates your ideas.

TEKS Process Standard (1)(D)

Problem 1 **Got It?** Analyzing $y = af(x)$ for $f(x) = \log_2 x$

Sketch the graph of each function along with the parent function $f(x) = \log_2 x$.

a. $y = \frac{1}{4}\log_2 x$

b. $y = 5\log_2 x$

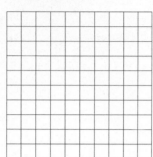 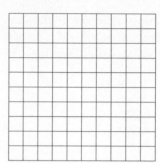

Learning Animation

ELPS Discuss the transformations you learned when working with functions. Make predictions about transformations of the *logarithmic function*. What operations on $y = \log_b x$ will result in the transformations you have already learned?

Problem 2 **Got It?** Analyzing $y = af(x)$ for $f(x) = \log_{10} x$

Sketch the graph of each function along with the parent function $f(x) = \log_{10} x$. Describe the effect of each transformation on the x-intercept.

a. $y = \frac{1}{5}\log_{10} x$

b. $y = \frac{3}{2}\log_{10} x$

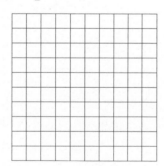

Learning Animation

Lesson 7-7 | Transformations of Logarithmic Functions

Problem 3 **Got It?** Analyzing $y = f(x) + d$ for $f(x) = \log_2 x$

Learning
Animation

Sketch the graph of each function along with the parent function $f(x) = \log_2 x$.
What is the effect of each transformation on the asymptote?

   a. $y = \log_2 x + 3$

   b. $y = \log_2 x - 4$

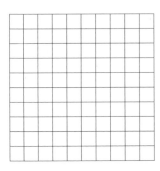

Problem 4 **Got It?** Analyzing $y = f(x) + d$ for $f(x) = \log_{10} x$

Learning
Animation

Sketch the graph of each function along with the parent function $f(x) = \log_{10} x$.
What is the effect of each transformation on the range?

   a. $y = \log_{10} x + 1$

   b. $y = \log_{10} x - 1$

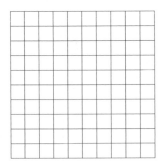

Lesson 7-7 | **Transformations of Logarithmic Functions**

TEKS Process Standard (1)(D)

 Problem 5 **Got It?** Analyzing $y = f(x - c)$ for $f(x) = \log_2 x$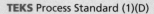

Sketch the graph of each function along with the parent function $f(x) = \log_2 x$.
Identify the vertical asymptote of each graph.

a. $y = \log_2(x - 2)$

b. $y = \log_2(x + 1)$

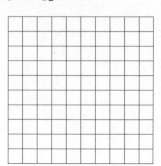 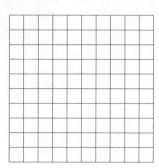

 Learning Animation

 Problem 6 **Got It?** Analyzing $y = f(x - c)$ for $f(x) = \log_{10} x$

Sketch the graph of each function along with the parent function $f(x) = \log_{10} x$.
What is the effect of each transformation on the domain?

a. $y = \log_{10}(x - 3)$

b. $y = \log_{10}(x + 0.5)$

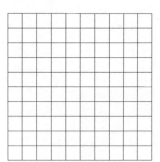 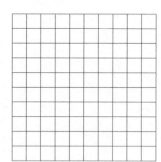

Learning Animation

Lesson 7-7 │ Transformations of Logarithmic Functions

Problem 7 **Got It?** Analyzing Change in Logarithmic Functions

The function modeling monthly profits P for a manufacturing firm is given by the formula $P(x) = 25 + \log_2(x - 10)$, where x represents the number of subscribers in hundreds. Describe how to use the parent function $f(x) = \log_2 x$ to sketch a graph of the profit function P.

Learning Animation

Do you know HOW?

Math Tools

Online Practice

Virtual Nerd Tutorials

1. Graph and label the parent function $y = \log_2 x$ and its transformations $y = \log_2 (x + 4)$ and $y = \log_2 x + 4$.

2. The graph shows a logarithmic parent function and a transformation of the function. Identify both functions.

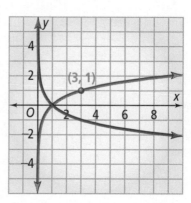

3. The profits in dollars from subscriptions to a local newspaper are shown by the formula $P(x) = -k + 60 \log_{10}(x)$, where x is the number of subscriptions sold and k is a constant. Find k if the newspaper makes a profit of \$35 from selling 100 subscriptions.

Do you UNDERSTAND?

Math
Tools

Online
Practice

Virtual Nerd
Tutorials

4. Vocabulary Give one example of a *logarithmic parent function* and a translation, stretch, compression, and reflection of that function.

5. Explain Mathematical Ideas (1)(G) The graph shows two functions: $y = \log_2 x$, and $y = \log_2 x + k$. First, explain how to find k from the graph, and identify k. Then, explain why the section of the graph that's very close to the y-axis is not useful for identifying k.

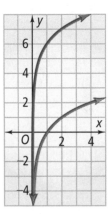

6. Analyze Mathematical Relationships (1)(F) A graph of $f(x) = \log_b x$ contains the point $(b, 1)$. Under a transformation of $f(x)$, the point $(b, 1)$ is transformed to $(b + 3, 2)$. What is the transformation of $f(x)$?

TEXAS Test Practice

Multiple Choice

For Exercises 1–4, choose the correct letter.

1. The graph of which function $g(x)$ is a translation of the graph of $f(x) = \log_2 x$ down 3 units and right 7 units?

   A. $g(x) = \log_2(x + 3) - 7$

   B. $g(x) = \frac{1}{7}\log_2 x - 3$

   C. $g(x) = \frac{1}{3}\log_2(x + 7)$

   D. $g(x) = \log_2(x - 7) - 3$

2. The graph of which logarithmic function has a vertical asymptote at the line $x = -4$?

   F. $y = \log_4 x$

   G. $y = \log_{10} x - 4$

   H. $y = \log_2(x - 4)$

   J. $y = \log_{10}(x + 4)$

3. The graph shows $y = \log_2 x$, and a second function that is a transformation of $y = \log_2 x$. What is the second function?

   A. $y = \frac{1}{5}\log_2 x$

   B. $y = 4\log_2 x$

   C. $y = \log_2(x - 2)$

   D. $y = -\log_2 x - 1$

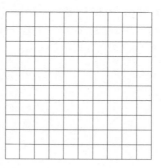

4. Which transformation maps $f(x) = 3\log_{10} x$ to $g(x) = -3\log_{10} x$?

   F. a reflection across the y-axis

   G. a stretch by a factor of 9

   H. a compression by a factor of $\frac{1}{3}$

   J. a reflection across the x-axis

Extended Response

5. Complete the table, and then graph the two functions. Describe the transformation that maps $f(x)$ to $g(x)$.

x	$f(x) = \log_3 x$	$g(x) = 0.5\log_3 x - 2$
0	undefined	
$\frac{1}{9}$		
$\frac{1}{3}$	-1	
1		
3		
9		-1

SOLVE IT!

A function *f* is bounded above if there is some number *B* that *f*(*x*) can never exceed. The exponential function base *e* shown here is not bounded above. Is the logarithmic function base *e* bounded above? If so, find a bounding number. If not, explain why.

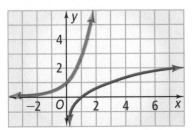

 Interactive Exploration

 Vocabulary Online

 Connect Mathematical Ideas (1)(F) What prior knowledge did you draw on to solve the problem?

TEKS Process Standard (1)(D)

 Problem 1 Got It? Domain, Range, Intercepts and Asymptotes of $y = \ln x$

Learning Animation

Sketch the graph of the function $f(x) = \ln x$. Describe three features of the graph that are characteristic of the graphs of all logarithmic functions.

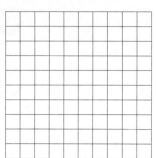

 Explain what effect, if any, the base b in $y = \log_b x$ has on the *domain, range, intercepts*, and *asymptotes*. Use what you know about transformations to explain what operations on the function $y = \log_e x$ affect the *domain, range, intercepts*, and *asymptotes*. Use this information to sketch the graph.

 Problem 2 Got It? Maximum and Minimum for a Given Interval of $f(x) = \log_e x$

Learning Animation

Find the maximum and minimum values of $f(x) = \log_e x$ over the interval $e \le x \le 10$.

TEKS Process Standard (1)(E)

Problem 3 Got It? Analyzing $y = af(x)$ for $f(x) = \log_e x$

Learning Animation

Sketch the graph of the function $g(x) = -\frac{1}{2}\log_e x$. Describe its transformation from the graph of the parent function, $f(x) = \log_e x$. What is the effect of the transformation on the x-intercept?

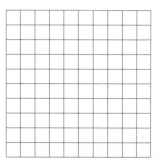

Lesson 7-8 | Attributes and Transformations of the Natural Logarithm Function

TEKS Process Standard (1)(E)

Problem 4   **Got It?**   Analyzing $y = f(x) + d$ for $f(x) = \log_e x$

Sketch the graph of the function $g(x) = \log_e x - 5$. Describe its transformation from the graph of the parent function, $f(x) = \log_e x$. Does the domain change?

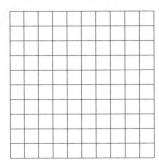

Learning Animation

TEKS Process Standard (1)(E)

Problem 5   **Got It?**   Analyzing $y = f(x - c)$ for $f(x) = \log_e x$

Sketch the graph of the function $g(x) = \log_e (x + 3)$. Describe its transformation from the graph of the parent function, $f(x) = \log_e x$. Does the asymptote change?

Learning Animation

Problem 6   **Got It?**   Using Transformations of Natural Logarithm Functions

The time T in years at which an investment is worth x dollars is given by the function $T = 0.25 \log_e x + 12$. Describe the graph of the function as a transformation of the graph of the parent function, $T = \log_e x$.

Learning Animation

Lesson 7-8 | Attributes and Transformations of the Natural Logarithm Function

271

Lesson Check

Do you know HOW?

1. Graph and label the functions $y = \log_e x$, $y = 3 \log_e x$, and $y = \frac{1}{3} \log_e x$.

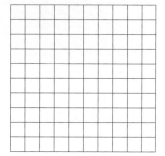

Math Tools

Online Practice

Virtual Nerd Tutorials

2. The graph shows $y = \log_e x$ and a transformation of the function. Identify the transformation.

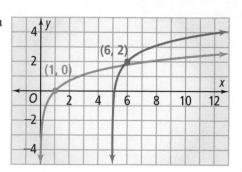

3. In an investment account, the time T_1 in years for which the account is worth x dollars is given by the function $T_1(x) = -32 + 20 \log_e x$. Describe the graph of this function as a transformation of the parent function, $T = \log_e x$.

Lesson Check

Do you UNDERSTAND?

Math
Tools

Online
Practice

Virtual Nerd
Tutorials

4. **Vocabulary** How is the notation for the natural logarithm function similar to the notation for the common logarithm?

5. **Analyze Mathematical Relationships (1)(F)** Compare the graphs of the parent function $f(x) = \log_e x$ to the graphs of $g(x) = 3\log_e x$; $h(x) = \log_e x + 3$; and $j(x) = \log_e(x + 3)$. Discuss their asymptotes and x-intercepts.

6. **Explain Mathematical Ideas (1)(G)** Let $f(x) = a\log_e x$, where a is a nonzero number. Explain how the knowing the value of a helps you find the maximum value of $f(x)$ over the interval $[10, 20]$ without graphing.

Lesson 7-8 | Attributes and Transformations of the Natural Logarithm Function

Multiple Choice

For Exercises 1–4, choose the correct letter.

1. The graph of which function $g(x)$ is a translation 5 units down from the graph of $f(x) = \log_e x$?

   A. $g(x) = \log_e x - 5$ **C.** $g(x) = \log_e(x - 5)$

   B. $g(x) = \frac{1}{5}\log_e x$ **D.** $g(x) = \log_e(x + 5)$

2. The graph of which logarithmic function has a vertical asymptote at the line $x = 1$?

   F. $y = \log_e x - 1$ **H.** $y = \log_e(x - 1)$

   G. $y = 2\log_e x - 1$ **J.** $y = \log_e(x + 1)$

3. The function shown in the graph is a translation of the parent function $y = \log_e x$. What is the function?

   A. $y = 5\log_e x$

   B. $y = \log_e(x - 5)$

   C. $y = \log_e(x - 6)$

   D. $y = \log_e x - 6$

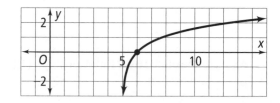

4. Which point is common to the graphs of $f(x) = \log_e x$ and $g(x) = a\log_e x$, for any real value of a?

   F. $(0, 1)$ **G.** (e, a) **H.** $(a, 0)$ **J.** $(1, 0)$

Extended Response

5. Complete the table, and then graph the two functions. Describe the transformation that maps $f(x)$ to $g(x)$.

x	$f(x) = \log_e x$	$g(x) = 2\log_e x + 1$
-1	undefined	
0		undefined
$\frac{1}{e}$		
1	0	
e		
e^2		5

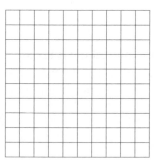

Lesson 7-8 | Attributes and Transformations of the Natural Logarithm Function

274

7-9 Exponential and Logarithmic Equations

 SOLVE IT!

You are a winner on a TV game show. Which prize would you choose? Explain.

Interactive Exploration

Vocabulary Online

 Create Representations to Communicate Mathematical Ideas (1)(E)
Describe how the representation you made successfully organizes and communicates your solution to the problem.

Problem 1 **Got It?** Solving an Exponential
Equation—Common Base

Learning
Animation

What is the solution of $27^{3x} = 81$?

 Problem 2 **Got It?** Solving an Exponential
Equation—Different Bases

Learning
Animation

a. What is the solution of $5^{2x} = 130$?

b. Why can't you use the same method you used in Problem 1 to solve
Problem 2?

ELPS Using what you heard in the lesson, what two methods are used for solving
exponential equations with different bases on each side? What is the first step in
determining which method to use? Which method would work for any case?

TEKS Process Standard (1)(C)

 Problem 3 | **Got It?** | Solving an Exponential Equation With a Graph or Table

Learning Animation

What is the solution of each exponential equation? Check your answer.

a. $7^{4x} = 800$

b. $5.2^{3x} = 400$

TEKS Process Standard (1)(A)

 Problem 4 | **Got It?** | Modeling With an Exponential Equation

Learning Animation

Your lumber company has 1,200,000 trees. After how many years will you have harvested half of the trees if you harvest 5% yearly?

Lesson 7-9 | Exponential and Logarithmic Equations

Problem 5 | Got It? | Solving a Logarithmic Equation

What is the solution of $\log(3 - 2x) = -1$?

Learning Animation

Problem 6 | Got It? | Using Logarithmic Properties to Solve an Equation

What is the solution of $\log 6 - \log 3x = -2$?

Learning Animation

Problem 7 | **Got It?** | Modeling With Logarithms

Use the function $t(x) = \frac{\log x - \log 120}{\log 1.3}$ from Problem 7. About how many years t will it take for the enrollment x to reach 500 students? Explain.

Learning
Animation

Lesson Check

Do you know HOW?

1. Solve for x.

$$\log 4x = 2$$

Math
Tools

Online
Practice

Virtual Nerd
Tutorials

2. Solve for x.

$$\log_2 x + \log_2 (x - 2) = 3$$

3. The population of algae in a beaker is estimated using the function $P(t) = 120(2)^t$, where $P(t)$ is the population after t weeks. After about how many days will the population be 800 algae?

Lesson Check

Do you UNDERSTAND?

Math Tools

Online Practice

Virtual Nerd Tutorials

4. Vocabulary How can an *exponential equation*, such as $y = ab^x$, be transformed into a *logarithmic equation*?

5. Evaluate Reasonableness (1)(B) Describe and correct the error made in solving the equation.

$$\log_2 x = 2 \log_3 9$$
$$\log_2 x = \log_3 9^2$$
$$x = 9^2$$
$$x = 81$$

6. Justify Mathematical Arguments (1)(G) Is it possible for an exponential equation to have no solution? If so, give an example. If not, explain why.

Lesson 7-9 | Exponential and Logarithmic Equations

281

TEXAS Test Practice

Multiple Choice

For Exercises 1–5, choose the correct letter.

1. The population of a town of 2000 people is increasing by 1% each year. At this rate, about how many years will it be until the population reaches 2700 people?

   A. 7   **B.** 20   **C.** 30   **D.** 70

2. If $3^{\log_2(8)-x} = 9$, what is the value of x?

   F. 1   **G.** 2   **H.** 3   **J.** 4

3. What is the solution of $\log_{10}(10^x) = 10$?

   A. 0   **B.** 1   **C.** 2   **D.** 10

4. Which best approximates the solution of $16^{2x} = 124$?

   F. 0.869   **G.** 1.150   **H.** 1.739   **J.** 3.477

5. Which equation represents the solution of $2^{3x+1} = 7$?

   A. $x = 3\left(\dfrac{\log 7}{\log 2} - 1\right)$ **C.** $x = \dfrac{1}{3}\left(\dfrac{\log 2}{\log 7} - 1\right)$

   B. $x = \dfrac{\log 7}{3\log 2} - 1$ **D.** $x = \dfrac{1}{3}\left(\dfrac{\log 7}{\log 2} - 1\right)$

Short Response

6. In 2007, the population of Tallahassee, Florida, was 168,979. Some researchers believe that the population of Tallahassee will increase at a rate of 1% each year for the 10 years following this.

   a. If the researchers are correct, how many years will it take for the population of Tallahassee to reach 180,000?

   b. Explain in words or show your work for how you determined the number of years found in part (a).

SOLVE IT!

You earn $800 at your summer job. You deposit the money into an account that pays 4% annual interest compounded continuously. To the nearest dollar, how much money will you have in the account after 5 years? Approximately how many years will it take for the amount of money in the account to reach $1100?

Interactive Exploration

Vocabulary Online

ATM Receipt

Starting Balance: $0

Deposit: $800.00

New Balance: $800.00

 Explain Mathematical Ideas (1)(G) A classmate questions your solution to the problem. Use precise mathematical language to explain why your solution is correct.

Problem 1 | Got It? | Simplifying a Natural Logarithmic Expression

What is each expression written as a single natural logarithm?

a. $\ln 7 + 2\ln 5$

b. $3\ln x - 2\ln 2x$

c. $3\ln x + 2\ln y + \ln 5$

Learning Animation

TEKS Process Standard (1)(F)

Problem 2 | Got It? | Solving a Natural Logarithmic Equation

What are the solutions of each equation? Check your answers.

a. $\ln x = 2$

b. $\ln (3x + 5)^2 = 4$

c. $\ln 2x + \ln 3 = 2$

Learning Animation

TEKS Process Standard (1)(F)

 Problem 3 Got It? Solving an Exponential Equation

What is the solution of each equation? Check your answers.

a. $e^{x-2} = 12$ **b.** $2e^{-x} = 20$ **c.** $e^{3x} + 5 = 15$

Learning Animation

 Problem 4 Got It? Using Natural Logarithms

a. A spacecraft can attain a stable orbit 300 km above Earth if it reaches a velocity of 7.7 km/s. The formula for a rocket's maximum velocity v in kilometers per second is $v = -0.0098t + c \ln R$. The booster rocket fires for t seconds, and the velocity of the exhaust is c km/s. The ratio of the mass of the rocket filled with fuel to its mass without fuel is R. A booster rocket for a spacecraft has a mass ratio of about 15, an exhaust velocity of 2.1 km/s, and a firing time of 30 s. Can the spacecraft achieve a stable orbit 300 km above Earth?

Learning Animation

b. Suppose a rocket, as designed, cannot provide enough velocity to achieve a stable orbit. Could alterations to the rocket make a stable orbit achievable? Explain.

ELPS Discuss the structure of the fifth sentence in part (a) with a classmate. Identify the subject and the predicate. What role do the two commas play in the sentence's structure? Work with your classmate to write three sentences that could replace it. Include the associated variable from the formula in each.

Do you know HOW?

1. Write each expression as a single natural logarithm.

    a. $4 \ln 3$ **b.** $\ln 18 - \ln 10$

    c. $\ln 3 + \ln 4$ **d.** $-2 \ln 2$

Math Tools

Online Practice

Virtual Nerd Tutorials

2. Solve each equation.

    a. $\ln (x - 7) = 2$ **b.** $\ln (2 - x) = 1$

3. The population of bacteria in a culture is given by $P(t) = 8000e^{\frac{t}{4.5}}$, where t is the time in days. When will the population be 48,000 bacteria?

Lesson Check

Do you UNDERSTAND?

Math Tools

Online Practice

Virtual Nerd Tutorials

4. **Vocabulary** How is the *natural logarithmic function* related to the function $y = e^x$?

5. **Evaluate Reasonableness (1)(B)** Describe how you could check the solution to the calculation to see that it's incorrect. Where is the error? Find the correct solution.

$$\ln 4x = 5$$
$$e^{\ln 4x} = e^5$$
$$4x = 5$$
$$x = \frac{5}{4}$$
$$x = 1.25$$

6. **Justify Mathematical Arguments (1)(G)** Can $\ln 5 + \log_2 10$ be written as a single logarithm? Explain your reasoning.

TEXAS Test Practice

Multiple Choice

For Exercises 1–4, choose the correct letter. Do not use a calculator.

1. Newton's Law of Cooling is modeled by $T(t) = T_r + (T_i - T_r)e^{kt}$, where $T(t)$ is the temperature of a heated substance t minutes after being removed from the heat source, T_i is the initial temperature, T_r is room temperature, and k is a constant. If the surface temperature of a pie right out of the oven is 350°F, room temperature is 70°F, and $k = -0.05$, about how many minutes will it take for the pie to cool to 100°F?

  A. 25   **B.** 35   **C.** 45   **D.** 55

2. When is it true that $\ln x = (\ln x)^2$?

  F. when $x = e$ or $x = 1$ **H.** when $x = e$ only

  G. when $x = 0$ or $x = 1$ **J.** This statement is never true.

3. What is $3 \ln 5 - \ln 2$ written as a single natural logarithm?

  A. $\ln 7.5$ **B.** $\ln 27$ **C.** $\ln\left(\frac{5}{2}\right)^3$ **D.** $\ln 62.5$

4. What is the solution of $\ln(x - 2)^2 = 6$?

  F. $2 + e^3$ **G.** $2 - e^3$ **H.** $2 \pm e^3$ **J.** $2 \pm e^6$

Short Response

5. The maximum velocity v of a rocket is $v = -0.0098t + c \ln R$. The rocket fires for t seconds and the velocity of the exhaust is c km/s. The ratio of the mass of the rocket filled with fuel to the mass of the rocket without fuel is R. A spacecraft can attain a stable orbit 300 km above Earth if it reaches a velocity of 7.7 km/s.

  a. What is the velocity of a spacecraft whose booster rocket has a mass ratio of 16, an exhaust velocity of 3.2 km/s, and a firing time of 40 s?

  b. Can this rocket attain a stable orbit 300 km above Earth? Explain in words or show work for how you determined your answer.

The first column shows a sequence of numbers. For 1st differences, subtract consecutive numbers in the sequence:

$-6 - (-4) = -2, \quad 4 - (-6) = 10, \quad$ and so on.

For 2nd differences, subtract consecutive 1st differences. For 3rd differences, subtract consecutive 2nd differences.

If the pattern suggested by the 3rd differences continues, what is the 8th number in the first column? Justify your reasoning.

Interactive Exploration

Vocabulary Online

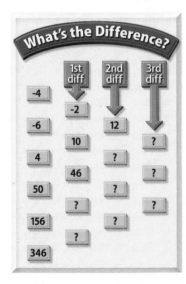

Use Representations to Communicate Mathematical Ideas (1)(E)
Describe how the representation you used to solve the problem successfully organizes and communicates your ideas.

Problem 1 **Got It?** Classifying Polynomials

Learning Animation

Write each polynomial in standard form. What is the classification of each by degree? By number of terms?

a. $3x^3 - x + 5x^4$

b. $3 - 4x^5 + 2x^2 + 10$

Problem 2 **Got It?** Describing End Behavior of Polynomial Functions

Learning Animation

Consider the leading term of $y = -4x^3 + 2x^2 + 7$. What is the end behavior of the graph?

Problem 3 | **Got It?** | **Graphing Cubic Functions**

What is the graph of each cubic function? Describe the graph.

a. $y = -x^3 + 2x^2 - x - 2$

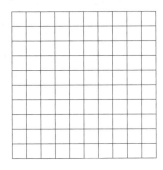

b. $y = x^3 - 1$

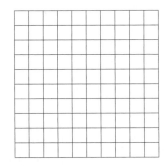

ELPS With a partner, restate what you heard in the lesson about classifying polynomials. What are the two methods that can be used? If a polynomial is written in standard form, where will you find the degree of the polynomial? Then have your partner summarize what you said and add any additional information.

 Problem 4 | **Got It?** | **Using Differences to Determine Degree**

a. What is the degree of the polynomial function that generates the data shown at the right?

b. What is an example of a polynomial function whose fifth differences are constant but whose fourth differences are not constant?

x	y
−3	23
−2	−16
−1	−15
0	−10
1	−13
2	−12
3	29

Lesson 8-1 | **Attributes of Polynomial Functions**

291

Do you know HOW?

Math Tools

Online Practice

Virtual Nerd Tutorials

1. Write the polynomial $x(7 - 4x^2)$ in standard form and then classify it by degree and number of terms.

2. Write the equation for the volume of a box with a length that is 4 less than the width and a height that is twice the width. Graph the equation.

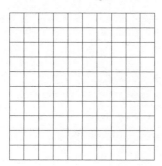

3. A polynomial function has three turning points. What are the possible degrees of the polynomial?

Lesson Check

Do you UNDERSTAND?

4. Vocabulary Describe the end behavior of the graph of $y = -4x^3 + 2$.

Math Tools

Online Practice

Virtual Nerd Tutorials

5. Use Representations to Communicate Mathematical Ideas (1)(E) Can the graph of a polynomial function be a straight line? If so, give an example.

6. Evaluate Reasonableness (1)(B) Your friend claims the graph of the function $y = 4x^3 + 4$ has only one turning point. How can you show that your friend's claim is unreasonable without graphing the function?

TEXAS Test Practice

Multiple Choice

For Exercises 1–7, choose the correct letter.

1. You are calculating the volume of a box which has a width of x inches, a length 1 inch less than the width, and a height 2 inches less than the width. What is the end behavior of the polynomial function that models the volume as a function of x?

A. up and down   **C.** down and down

B. down and up   **D.** up and up

2. How many terms are in the standard form of the polynomial $(2a - a^2)(a^2 - a)$?

F. 2   **G.** 3   **H.** 4   **J.** 5

3. Which expression is a binomial?

A. $2x$ **B.** $\frac{x}{2}$ **C.** $3x^2 + 2x + 4$ **D.** $x - 9$

4. What is the degree of the polynomial $5x + 4x^2 + 3x^3 - 5x$?

F. 1   **G.** 2   **H.** 3   **J.** 4

5. In the polynomial $x^2 + 1$, you replace x with $x - 1$. Which of the following is true?

A. The degree of the polynomial has changed.

B. The number of terms in the polynomial in standard form has changed.

C. The end behavior of the polynomial has changed.

D. None of the above has changed.

6. What is the standard form of the polynomial $9x^2 + 5x + 27 + 2x^3$?

F. $27 + 5x + 9x^2 + 2x^3$ **H.** $9x^2 + 5x + 27 + 2x^3$

G. $9x^2 + 5x + 2x^3 + 27$ **J.** $2x^3 + 9x^2 + 5x + 27$

7. What is the end behavior of $y = (nx^2)(mx)$, if $n > 0$ and $m < 0$?

A. down and down   **C.** down and up

B. up and up   **D.** up and down

Short Response

8. Simplify $(9x^3 - 4x + 2) - (x^3 + 3x^2 + 1)$. Then name the polynomial by degree and the number of terms.

SOLVE IT!

Your friend invests \$500 in a stock account. He knows the value of a stock can rise and fall. Suppose that over the first year the value of the stock gains p percent, and over the second year it loses p percent. The expression shown represents the value of the account after two years. Will your friend make money or lose money over the two-year period? Explain.

Interactive Exploration

Vocabulary Online

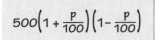

$$500\left(1 + \frac{p}{100}\right)\left(1 - \frac{p}{100}\right)$$

 Apply Mathematics (1)(A) Describe another real-world situation for which you could apply the same mathematical model.

Lesson 8-2 | Adding, Subtracting, and Multiplying Polynomials

Problem 1 **Got It?** Adding Polynomials

Learning
Animation

a. What is the sum of $-8x^2 + 2x + 1$ and $10x^2 - x$?

b. Explain why the sum of two polynomials P_1 and P_2 must also be a polynomial.

ELPS With a classmate, make a list of the things you have heard about polynomials. What questions can you ask that will help you understand the material more thoroughly? Explain the difference between a *term* and a *monomial*.

Lesson 8-2 │ Adding, Subtracting, and Multiplying Polynomials

Problem 2 | Got It? | Subtracting Polynomials

What is the difference $(5x^2 + 7x - 8) - (7x^3 + 2x^2 + 3x)$?

Learning Animation

Problem 3 | Got It? | Multiplying Polynomials

What is each product?

a. $(a - 2b)(4a + 5b)$

Learning Animation

b. $(5y^2 - 2y - 1)(y + 4)$

c. $(x - 1)(x + 1)(5x - 6)$

Lesson Check

Do you know HOW?

Math
Tools

Online
Practice

Virtual Nerd
Tutorials

1. Simplify the expression $(x + 4)(5x - 7) - (3x^2 + 8x - 6)$.

2. The length ℓ of a rectangle is 5 centimeters longer than twice the width w. Write expressions to show the area and the perimeter of the rectangle in terms of w.

3. A store manager buys a case of 200 mechanical pencils for $27.00. She plans to sell them at first for $0.75 each, and then to lower the price to $0.50 each. Write a simplified expression to express the profit from selling all of the pencils, if x pencils are sold at the lower price.

Lesson Check

Do you UNDERSTAND?

Math Tools

Online Practice

Virtual Nerd Tutorials

4. **Vocabulary** Given the binomials $x + a$ and $x - b$, how would you find the product?

5. **Select Techniques to Solve Problems (1)(C)** Explain two ways to subtract two polynomials.

6. **Explain Mathematical Ideas (1)(G)** Is the set of polynomials closed under multiplication? Explain.

TEXAS Test Practice

Multiple Choice

For Exercises 1–5, choose the correct letter.

1. There is a circular garden in the middle of a square yard. The radius of the circle is $4x$. The side length of the yard is $20x$. What is the area of the part of the yard that is not covered by the circle?

   A. $4x(5)$ **B.** $8x^2(5 - \pi)$ **C.** $16x(25 + \pi)$ **D.** $16x^2(25 - \pi)$

2. A composite shape is formed out of two rectangles. One has area $4j^2 + 6$ and the other has area $2j^2 - 3$. What is the total area of the shape?

   F. $6j^2 - 3$ **G.** $6j^2 + 3$ **H.** $6j^2 + 9$ **J.** $4j^4 + 3$

3. What is the difference of the following polynomials?

$$6x^3 - 2x^2 + 4$$
$$\underline{-(2x^3 + 4x^2 - 5)}$$

   A. $4x^3 - 2x^2 - 1$ **C.** $4x^3 - 2x^2 + 1$

   B. $8x^3 + 6x^2 - 1$ **D.** $4x^3 - 6x^2 + 9$

4. Let $f(x) = 2x - 3$, $g(x) = 5x$, and $h(x) = x^2$. Which of the following is the simplified form of $h(x) \cdot (g(f(x)))$?

   F. $5x^2 + 2x - 3$ **G.** $10x^3 - 15x^2$ **H.** $-5x^2$ **J.** $7x^3 - 15x^2$

5. What is the simplified form of $-3z^2(z + 2) - 4(z^2 + 1)$?

   A. $-7z^2 + 1$ **C.** $-3z^3 - 2z^2 - 4$

   B. $-3z^3 - 4z^2 - 6z - 4$ **D.** $-3z^3 - 10z^2 - 4$

Short Response

6. A rectangular soccer field with a length of $5x$ and a width of $9x$ has been marked inside a rectangular field that has a length of $5x + 12$ and a width of $9x + 14$.

   a. What is the area of the part of the field that is outside the soccer field? Factor your answer.

   b. There is a semicircular fountain in the rectangular field that has a radius of $2x$. What is the area of the part of the field that does not include the soccer field or the fountain? Factor your answer.

SOLVE IT!

Scan page for an interactive version of this Solve It.

The graphs of $y = x - 1$ and $y = x + 1$ are shown. For any value of x, identify the corresponding point on each line. Then locate a new point with a y-coordinate that is the *product* of the y-coordinates of the points on the lines. What pattern do you see? What would the graph of *all* product points look like?

Interactive Exploration

Vocabulary Online

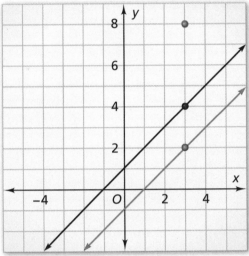

 Connect Mathematical Ideas (1)(F) How does this problem relate to a problem you have seen before?

Problem 1 | **Got It?** | **Writing a Polynomial Function in Factored Form**

What is the factored form of $y = x^3 - x^2 - 12x$?

Learning
Animation

 Problem 2 | **Got It?** | **Finding Zeros of a Polynomial Function**

What are the zeros of $f(x) = x(x - 3)(x + 5)$? Graph the function.

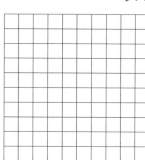

Learning
Animation

Lesson 8-3 | Polynomials, Linear Factors, and Zeros

TEKS Process Standard (1)(G)

 Problem 3 | **Got It?** | Writing a Polynomial Function From Its Zeros

a. What is a quadratic polynomial function with zeros 3 and -3?

b. What is a cubic polynomial function with zeros 3, 3, and -3?

c. Graph both functions. How do the graphs differ? How are they similar?

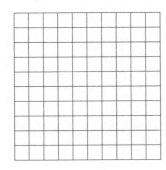

ELPS Discuss with a classmate facts about the graphs or functions from the Got It. Write down the main points. Then compare the graphs or functions by linking your statements with connecting words such as: *just as, because, however, that is why, even though, clearly, then, before,* and *likewise.*

Problem 4 | **Got It?** | **Finding the Multiplicity of a Zero**

What is the factored form of $f(x) = x^3 - 4x^2 + 4x$? What are the zeros? What are the multiplicities of the zeros? How does the graph behave at these zeros?

Learning Animation

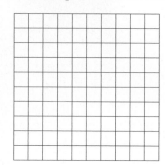

Lesson 8-3 | Polynomials, Linear Factors, and Zeros

Problem 5 | **Got It?** | Identifying a Relative Maximum and Minimum

Learning
Animation

What are the relative maximum and minimum of $f(x) = 3x^3 + x^2 - 5x$?

 Problem 6 | **Got It?** | Using a Polynomial Function to Maximize Volume

Learning
Animation

A camera's length is equal to 1.5 times its height. What is the maximum volume of the camera, if the sum of the dimensions is at most 4 inches?

Lesson Check

Do you know HOW?

1. Use a graphing calculator to find the relative maximum and relative minimum of the graph of $f(x) = x^3 + \frac{3}{2}x^2 - 5x - 2$.

 Math Tools

 Online Practice

 Virtual Nerd Tutorials

2. The graph of polynomial function $f(x)$ is shown here. What are its zeros? Use the zeros to write $f(x)$ in factored form. Assume the coefficient of the x^3 term is 1.

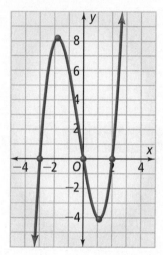

3. The volume V of a certain rectangular box is defined by the function $V(w) = 2w^3 - 7w^2 - 30w$, where w is the width. Factor $V(w)$ and use the formula $V = \ell wh$ to find the height h and length ℓ of the box in terms of w. Assume $h > \ell$. What is a realistic domain for $V(w)$? Explain.

Lesson Check

Do you UNDERSTAND?

4. **Vocabulary** Write a polynomial function h, in standard form that has 3 and -5 as zeros of multiplicity 2.

5. **Explain Mathematical Ideas (1)(G)** How does the graph of a polynomial function behave at zeros of multiplicity 1? How does the graph behave at zeros of multiplicity 2?

6. **Explain Mathematical Ideas (1)(G)** Your friend says that to write a function that has zeros 3 and -1, you should multiply the two factors $x + 3$ and $x - 1$ to get $f(x) = x^2 + 2x - 3$. Describe and correct your friend's error.

TEXAS Test Practice

Multiple Choice

For Exercises 1–5, choose the correct letter.

1. The volume of a box is represented by the polynomial function $y = (x - 3)(2x + 1)(x - 1)$. What values of x will make the volume of the box equal to zero?

   A. $\frac{1}{2}, 1, 3$ **B.** $-1, 1, 3$ **C.** $-\frac{1}{2}, 1, 3$ **D.** $-3, \frac{1}{2}, -1$

2. What are the linear factors of $2x^3 + 5x^2 - 12x$?

   F. $x + 4$ and $2x - 3$ **H.** $x, x + 4$, and $2x - 3$

   G. $x - 4$ and $2x + 3$ **J.** $x, x - 4$, and $2x + 3$

3. Which is the cubic polynomial in standard form with roots 3, −6, and 0?

   A. $x^2 - 3x - 18$ **C.** $x^3 - 3x^2 - 18x$

   B. $x^2 + 3x - 18$ **D.** $x^3 + 3x^2 - 18x$

4. A shipping company charges an oversize package fee if the sum of the dimensions of the package are more than 60 in. The length of the package you want to send must be twice its width. What are the dimensions of a package with maximum volume that avoids the oversize fee?

   F. width = 2 in.   **H.** width = 20 in.
   length = 4 in.   length = 20 in.
   height = 54 in.   height = 20 in.

   G. width = 13.33 in.   **J.** width = 13.33 in.
   length = 6.67 in.   length = 26.66 in.
   height = 40 in.   height = 20.01 in.

5. What is the multiplicity of the zero of the polynomial function that represents the volume of a sphere with radius $x + 5$?

   A. 3   **B.** 5   **C.** π **D.** 125

Short Response

6. A rectangular box is 24 in. long, 12 in. wide, and 18 in. high. If each dimension is increased by x in., what is the polynomial function in standard form that models the volume V of the box? Show your work.

SOLVE IT!

Can you arrange all of these pieces to make a rectangle with no pieces overlapping and no gaps? If you can, make a sketch. If you cannot, explain why.

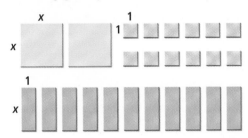

Interactive Exploration

Vocabulary Online

Use Multiple Representations to Communicate Mathematical Ideas (1)(D)
What is another representation you could use to present your solution? Explain how the representation communicates the same information.

Problem 1 **Got It?** Solving Polynomial Equations Using Factors

Learning Animation

What are the real or imaginary solutions of each equation?

a. $(x^2 - 1)(x^2 + 4) = 0$

b. $x^5 + 4x^3 = 5x^4 - 2x^3$

 Problem 2 **Got It?** Solving Polynomial Equations by Factoring

Learning Animation

What are the real or imaginary solutions of each polynomial equation?

a. $x^4 = 16$

b. $x^3 = 8x - 2x^2$

ELPS Discuss the terms *polynomial equation, solution, real,* and *imaginary* with a classmate. Go back through the lesson to find definitions, concepts, and illustrations. Then work together to design a concept map summarizing each term and the steps you take to solve polynomial equations.

Lesson 8-4 | Solving Polynomial Equations

310

Problem 3 | **Got It?** | Factoring the Sum of Two Cubes

What are the linear and quadratic factors for the polynomial expression $8x^3 + 125$?

Learning Animation

 Problem 4 | **Got It?** | Sums and Differences of Cubes

a. Factor $64x^3y + 125y^4$. What are the linear and quadratic factors of the expression?

Learning Animation

b. Factor $16x^4 - 54x$. What are the linear and quadratic factors of the expression?

Lesson 8-4 │ Solving Polynomial Equations

Problem 5 | **Got It?** | **Factoring Polynomials by Grouping**

Factor $x^4 + 3x^3 + x^2 + 3x$ by grouping. What are the linear and quadratic factors of the expression?

Learning Animation

Problem 6 | **Got It?** | Solving Polynomial Equations Using a Difference of Two Cubes

Learning Animation

What are the real or imaginary solutions of $x(x^2 + 8) = 8(x + 1)$?

Lesson Check

Do you know HOW?

1. What are the real or imaginary solutions of $x^3 - 12 = 3x^2 - 4x$?

Math Tools

Online Practice

Virtual Nerd Tutorials

2. What are three consecutive integers whose product is 693 more than their sum?

3. Factor $x^4 - 3x^3 + 8x - 24$.

Lesson Check

Do you UNDERSTAND?

 Math Tools

 Online Practice

 Virtual Nerd Tutorials

4. **Vocabulary** Identify each expression as a sum of cubes, difference of cubes, or difference of squares.

   a. $x^2 - 64$

   b. $x^3 + 8$

   c. $x^3 - 125$

   d. $x^2 - 81$

5. **Select Techniques to Solve Problems (1)(C)** Which method of solving polynomial equations will not identify the imaginary roots? Explain.

6. **Use Multiple Representations to Communicate Mathematical Ideas (1)(D)** Show how to find the real solutions of the polynomial equation $0 = x^6 - x^2$ using two different methods. Show your steps.

TEXAS Test Practice

Multiple Choice

For Exercises 1–6, choose the correct letter.

1. Over 3 years, you save \$550, \$600, and \$650 from babysitting jobs. The polynomial $550x^3 + 600x^2 + 650x$ represents your total bank account balance after 3 years. The annual interest rate is $x - 1$. What is the interest rate needed so that you will have \$2000 after 3 years?

   A. 0.06%   **B.** 1.06%   **C.** 5.52%   **D.** 24%

2. The product of three integers x, $x + 2$, and $x - 5$ is 240. What are the integers?

   F. 5.9, 7.9, 0.9   **G.** 7.5, 9.5, 2.5   **H.** 5, 6, 8   **J.** 8, 10, 3

3. If you factor $x^3 - 8$ in the form $(x - a)(x^2 + bx + c)$, what is the value of a?

   A. 2   **B.** -2 **C.** 4   **D.** -4

4. Which polynomial equation has the zeros 5, -3, and $\frac{1}{2}$?

   F. $x^3 + 4x^2 + 4x - 45$ **H.** $2x^3 - 5x^2 - 28x + 15$

   G. $x^3 - 4x^2 + 4x + 15$ **J.** $2x^3 + 5x^2 - 28x - 45$

5. Your brother is 3 years older than you. Your sister is 4 years younger than you. The product of your ages is 1872. How old is your sister?

   A. 9 years   **B.** 13 years   **C.** 16 years   **D.** 17 years

6. What are the real roots of $x^3 + 8 = 0$?

   F. 2   **G.** -2 **H.** $-2 \pm \sqrt{3}$ **J.** $-2 \pm \sqrt{5}$

Short Response

7. You have a block of wood with a depth of x units, a length of $5x$ units, and a height of $2x$ units. You need to cut a slice off the top of the block to decrease the height by 2 units. The new block will have a volume of 480 cubic units.

   a. What are the dimensions of the new block?

   b. What is the volume of the slice?

SOLVE IT!

In how many ways is it possible to replace the squares with single-digit numbers to complete a correct division problem? Justify your answer.

Interactive Exploration

Vocabulary Online

 Use Representations to Communicate Mathematical Ideas (1)(E)
Describe how the representation you used to solve the problem successfully organizes and communicates your ideas.

Problem 1 | **Got It?** | **Using Polynomial Long Division**

Use polynomial long division to divide $3x^3 - 8x^2 - 21x + 56$ by $x^2 - 7$. What are the quotient and remainder?

Learning Animation

TEKS Process Standard (1)(G)

 Problem 2 | **Got It?** | **Using Polynomial Long Division to Check Factors**

a. Is $x^2 - 1$ a factor of $P(x) = x^4 + 4x^2 - 5$? If it is, write $P(x)$ as the product of two factors.

Learning Animation

b. Use the fact that $12 \cdot 31 = 372$ to write the polynomial $3x^2 + 7x + 2$ as the product of two factors.

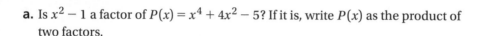

 Problem 3 | **Got It?** | **Using Synthetic Division**

Use synthetic division to divide $x^4 - 49x^2 - 8x + 56$ by $x - 7$. What are the quotient and remainder?

Learning Animation

Lesson 8-5 | Dividing Polynomials

318

TEKS Process Standard (1)(A)

Problem 4 | Got It? | Using Synthetic Division to Solve a Problem

If the polynomial $x^3 + 6x^2 + 11x + 6$ expresses the volume, in cubic inches, of a box, and the width is $x + 1$ in., what are the dimensions of the box?

Learning Animation

ELPS Read the Got It with a classmate. Use a rectangular box as visual support for solving the problem. What do the expressions in the problem represent for the box? What dimensions are missing? How do you solve for the missing dimensions?

Problem 5 | Got It? | Evaluating a Polynomial

Given that $P(x) = x^4 - 3x^3 - 28x^2 + 5x + 20$, what is $P(-4)$?

Learning Animation

Lesson Check

Do you know HOW?

Math Tools

Online Practice

Virtual Nerd Tutorials

1. Divide $x^3 + 5x^2 + 11x + 15$ by $x + 3$ using any method.

2. When a polynomial is divided by $5x + 7$, the quotient is $2x^3 - 4x + 2$ with remainder 1. Find the polynomial.

3. The remainder from the division of the polynomial $3x^3 + 6x^2 - rx + 18$ by $x + 2$ is 26. What is the value of r?

Lesson Check

Do you UNDERSTAND?

Math Tools

Online Practice

Virtual Nerd Tutorials

4. **Analyze Mathematical Relationships (1)(F)** A polynomial $P(x)$ is divided by a binomial $x - a$. The remainder is 0. What conclusion can you draw? Explain your answer.

5. **Use a Problem-Solving Model (1)(B)** Explain why it is important to have the terms of both polynomials written in descending order of degree before dividing.

6. **Create Representations to Communicate Mathematical Ideas (1)(E)** Write a polynomial division that has a quotient of $x + 3$ and a remainder of 2.

TEXAS Test Practice

Gridded Response

Solve each exercise and enter your answer in the grid provided.

1. The volume of a box is given by $4x^3 + 8x^2 + x - 3$, and its height is given by $x + 1$. Calculate the area of the bottom of the box (that is, the length times width). What is the leading coefficient of the polynomial representing the area of the box?

2. What is the missing value in the following synthetic division?

$$
\begin{array}{r|rrrrr}
-4 & 1 & 0 & -5 & 4 & 12 \\
   &   & -4 & \boxed{} & -44 & 160 \\
\hline
   & 1 & -4 & 11 & -40 & 172 \\
\end{array}
$$

3. What is the remainder when you divide $x^4 - 9x^3 + 27x^2 - 27x$ by $x - 3$?

4. How many unique factors does $x^4 + 4x^3 - 3x^2 - 14x - 8$ have, including $x + 4$?

1.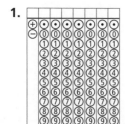

2.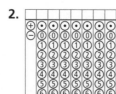

3.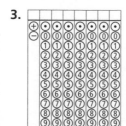

4.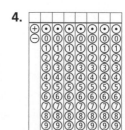

Lesson 8-5 | Dividing Polynomials

322

SOLVE IT!

I am greater than my square. The sum of my numerator and denominator is 5.

What fraction am I? How did you find me?

Interactive
Exploration

Vocabulary
Online

My numerator
is a factor of 6.

My denominator
is a factor of 4.

 Use a Problem-Solving Model (1)(B) Evaluate your problem-solving model. Which parts were helpful? Which would you want to revise? Explain.

Problem 1 | **Got It?** | Finding a Rational Root

Learning Animation

What are the rational roots of $3x^3 + 7x^2 + 6x - 8 = 0$?

 ELPS Discuss the new expressions you heard in this lesson with a classmate. How can you use what you already know about rational numbers and roots of a polynomial to understand the expression *rational roots*? Work with your classmate to come up with a five-step process for identifying the rational roots of a polynomial.

TEKS Process Standard (1)(E)

 Problem 2 | **Got It?** | Using the Rational Root Theorem

Learning Animation

What are the rational roots of $2x^3 + x^2 - 7x - 6 = 0$?

Lesson 8-6 | Theorems About Roots of Polynomial Equations

Problem 3 | **Got It?** | **Using the Conjugate Root Theorem to Identify Roots**

Learning Animation

A cubic polynomial $P(x)$ has real coefficients. If $3 - 2i$ and $\frac{5}{2}$ are two roots of $P(x) = 0$, what is one additional root?

 Problem 4 | **Got It?** | **Using Conjugates to Construct a Polynomial**

Learning Animation

What quartic polynomial equation has roots $2 - 3i$, 8, 2?

TEKS Process Standard (1)(F)

 Problem 5 | **Got It?** | **Using Descartes' Rule of Signs**

Learning Animation

a. What does Descartes' Rule of Signs tell you about the real roots of
$2x^4 - x^3 + 3x^2 - 1 = 0$?

b. Can you confirm real and complex roots graphically? Explain.

Do you know HOW?

Math Tools

Online Practice

Virtual Nerd Tutorials

1. Use the Rational Root Theorem to list all possible rational roots for the equation $2x^3 - x^2 - 6$.

2. Find all the rational roots of $P(x) = x^4 - x^2 = 0$. Does this match what Descartes' Rule of Signs tells you about the real roots? Explain.

3. Use the Conjugate Root Theorem to find all roots of $P(x) = x^4 - 1$.

Lesson Check

Do you UNDERSTAND?

4. **Vocabulary** Give an example of a conjugate pair.

Math
Tools

Online
Practice

Virtual Nerd
Tutorials

5. **Analyze Mathematical Relationships (1)(F)** In the statements below, r and s represent integers. Is each statement *always*, *sometimes*, or *never* true? Explain your answer.

   a. A root of the equation $3x^3 + rx^2 + sx + 8 = 0$ could be 5.

   b. A root of the equation $3x^3 + rx^2 + sx + 8 = 0$ could be -2.

6. **Evaluate Reasonableness (1)(B)** A student claims that $-4i$ is the only imaginary root of a polynomial equation that has real coefficients. What is the student's mistake?

Lesson 8-6 | Theorems About Roots of Polynomial Equations

TEXAS Test Practice

Multiple Choice

For Exercises 1–5, choose the correct letter.

1. What does Descartes' Rule of Signs tell you about the real roots of $6x^4 + 29x^3 + 40x^2 + 7x - 12$?

   A. 1 positive real root and 1 or 3 negative real roots

   B. 0 positive real roots and 1 negative real root

   C. 1 or 3 positive real roots and 1 negative real root

   D. 0 or 1 positive real roots and 3 negative real roots

2. A quartic polynomial $P(x)$ has rational coefficients. If $\sqrt{7}$ and $6 + i$ are roots of $P(x) = 0$, what is one additional root?

   F. 7   G. $-\sqrt{7}$ H. $i - 6$ J. $6i$

3. What is a quartic polynomial function with rational coefficients that has roots i and $2i$?

   A. $x^4 - 5x^2 - 4$ B. $x^4 - 5x^2 + 4$ C. $x^4 + 5x^2 + 4$ D. $x^4 + 5x^2 - 4$

4. A fourth-degree polynomial with integer coefficients has roots at 1 and $3 + \sqrt{5}$. Which number *cannot* also be a root of this polynomial?

   F. -1 G. -3 H. $3 - \sqrt{5}$ J. $3 + \sqrt{2}$

5. What is a rational root of $x^3 + 3x^2 - 6x - 8 = 0$?

   A. 1   B. -1 C. 8   D. -8

Extended Response

6. A third-degree polynomial with rational coefficients has roots -4 and $-4i$. If the leading coefficient of the polynomial is $\frac{3}{2}$, what is the polynomial? Show your work.

PearsonTEXAS.com

SOLVE IT!

The first graph shows the three complex-number solutions of $x^3 - 1 = 0$. The second graph shows the six solutions of $x^6 - 1 = 0$. How many complex number solutions does $x^{12} - 1 = 0$ have? What are they?

Interactive Exploration

Vocabulary Online

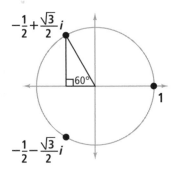

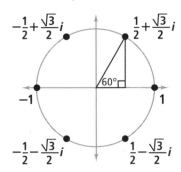

Explain Mathematical Ideas (1)(G) A classmate questions your solution to the problem. Use precise mathematical language to explain why your solution is correct.

Problem 1 | **Got It?** | **Using the Fundamental Theorem of Algebra**

What are all the roots of the equation $x^4 + 2x^3 = 13x^2 - 10x$?

Learning
Animation

Problem 2 | **Got It?** | Finding All the Zeros of a Polynomial Function

 Learning Animation

a. Find the factored form of the function $g(x) = 2x^4 - 3x^3 - x - 6$. Identify the linear and quadratic factors. What are the zeros of $g(x)$?

b. The graph of $f(x) = x^5 + 4x^4 - 3x^3 - 12x^2 - 4x - 4$ is shown at the right.

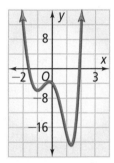

    i. Use the turning points to explain why the graph does NOT show all of the real zeros of the function.

    ii. The graph of $g(x) = f(x) + 4$ is a translation of the graph of f up 4 units. How many real zeros of g will the graph of g show? Explain.

 ELPS Discuss with a classmate. Make a list of key words and expressions you need to know before solving the Got It, such as *roots*, *zeros*, *real roots*, and *turning points*. How are these terms related? How are they different? Go back through your text to review definitions and information that will aid your discussion.

Lesson Check

Do you know HOW?

1. Find the number of roots of each equation.

   a. $5x^4 + 12x^3 - x^2 + 3x + 5 = 0$

   b. $-x^{14} - x^8 - x + 7 = 0$

2. Find all the roots of $x^3 - 5x^2 + 16x - 80$.

3. Write a polynomial function of degree 4 with rational coefficients and two complex zeros of multiplicity 2.

Math Tools

Online Practice

Virtual Nerd Tutorials

Lesson Check

Do you UNDERSTAND?

Math Tools

Online Practice

Virtual Nerd Tutorials

4. Vocabulary Given a polynomial equation of degree n, explain how you determine the number of roots of the equation.

5. Evaluate Reasonableness (1)(B) Can the set of roots of a polynomial of degree 3 include $1 - i$, $1 + i$, and i? Explain.

6. Select Techniques to Solve Problems (1)(C) Describe when to use synthetic division and when to use the Quadratic Formula to determine the linear factors of a polynomial.

Multiple Choice

For Exercises 1–6, choose the correct letter.

1. A classmate claims that if a polynomial with real coefficients has roots of 6, -2, $-4i$, and $\sqrt{5}$, then $-\sqrt{5}$ must be another root of the polynomial. Is your classmate correct? Explain.

   A. Yes, because $\sqrt{5}$ and $-\sqrt{5}$ make a conjugate pair.

   B. Yes, because the polynomial must have exactly 5 roots according to the Fundamental Theorem of Algebra.

   C. Yes, because $\sqrt{5}$ and $-\sqrt{5}$ are not a conjugate pair.

   D. Yes, because the other root must be $4i$.

2. One root of the equation $x^3 + x^2 - 2 = 0$ is 1. What are the other two roots?

   F. $-1 \pm i$ **G.** $1 \pm 2i$ **H.** $\pm 1 + 2i$ **J.** $\pm 1 - i$

3. A polynomial with real coefficients has 3, $2i$, and $-i$ as three of its zeros. What is the least possible degree of the polynomial?

   A. 3   **B.** 4   **C.** 5   **D.** 6

4. How many times does the graph of $x^3 + 27$ cross the x-axis?

   F. 0   **G.** 1   **H.** 2   **J.** 3

5. Which of the following is the polynomial with zeros at 1, $-\frac{3}{2}$, $2i$, and $-2i$?

   A. $2x^4 + x^3 + 5x^2 + 4x - 12$ **C.** $2x^4 + x^3 - 11x^2 - 4x + 12$

   B. $2x^4 - x^3 + 5x^2 - 4x - 12$ **D.** $2x^4 - x^3 - 11x^2 + 4x + 12$

6. Which number is a zero of $f(x) = x^3 + 6x^2 + 9x$ with multiplicity 1?

   F. -3 **G.** 0   **H.** 1   **J.** 3

Short Response

7. One root of the equation $x^4 - 4x^3 - 6x^2 + 4x + 5 = 0$ is -1.

   a. How many complex roots does this equation have?

   b. What are all the roots? Show your work.

SOLVE IT!

This equation contains an infinite radical. Square each side. You get a quadratic equation. Are the two solutions of the quadratic equation also solutions of this equation? Explain your reasoning.

$$x = \sqrt{1 + \sqrt{1 + \sqrt{1 + \ldots}}}$$

Interactive Exploration

Vocabulary Online

 Analyze Mathematical Relationships (1)(F) What mathematical relationships did you identify in the problem? How did you use them to solve the problem?

Problem 1 **Got It?** **Finding All Real Roots**

Learning Animation

a. What are the real fifth roots of 0, -1, and 32?

b. What are the real square roots of 0.01, -1, and $\frac{36}{121}$?

c. Explain why a negative real number b has no real nth roots if n is even.

Problem 2 **Got It?** **Finding Roots**

Learning Animation

What is each real-number root?

a. $\sqrt[3]{-27}$

b. $\sqrt[4]{-81}$

c. $\sqrt{(-7)^2}$

d. $\sqrt{-49}$

TEKS Process Standard (1)(D)

 Problem 3 | **Got It?** | **Simplifying Radical Expressions**

What is the simplified form of each radical expression?

 Learning Animation

a. $\sqrt{81x^4}$

b. $\sqrt[3]{a^{12}b^{15}}$

c. $\sqrt[4]{x^{12}y^{16}}$

TEKS Process Standard (1)(A)

 Problem 4 | **Got It?** | **Using a Radical Expression**

A teacher's formula for adjusting test scores is $A = 10\sqrt{R}$, where A is the adjusted score and R is the raw score. What are the adjusted scores for raw scores of 0 and 100?

 Learning Animation

ELPS Share your opinion about adjusting class scores. This is one teacher's formula for adjusting scores. Do you think this is the best formula? What is another formula you could use for adjusting the grades? Which is best? Why?

Lesson 9-1 │ Roots and Radical Expressions

337

Lesson Check

Do you know HOW?

1. Simplify the radical expression $\sqrt{a^8 b^{18}}$.

2. Write a radical expression involving a fifth root that can be simplified to $-2x^2 y^3$.

3. A company manufactures cylindrical storage containers for which the radius is equal to the height. The equation $r = \sqrt[3]{\frac{V}{\pi}}$ relates the radius r of a container, in inches, and the volume V, in cubic inches. The manager of the company decides to decrease the volume of a container from 343π in.^{3} to 216π in.^{3}. By how much does the radius of the container decrease?

Math Tools

Online Practice

Virtual Nerd Tutorials

Lesson Check

Do you UNDERSTAND?

Math Tools

Online Practice

Virtual Nerd Tutorials

4. **Vocabulary** Explain the difference between a real root and the principal root.

5. **Explain Mathematical Ideas (1)(G)** A student said that the only fourth root of 16 is 2. Is the student correct? Explain.

6. **Analyze Mathematical Relationships (1)(F)** A nonzero number has only one real nth root. What can you conclude about the index n?

TEXAS Test Practice

Multiple Choice

For Exercises 1–6, choose the correct letter.

1. The formula for the volume of a sphere is $V = \frac{4\pi}{3}r^3$, where r is the radius of the sphere. If a spherical balloon can be inflated with 100 in.^{3} of air, approximately what is the radius of the balloon?

   A. 3 in.   **B.** 6 in.   **C.** 9 in.   **D.** 12 in.

2. x is a number greater than zero. Which of the following expressions is not equal to x?

   F. $\sqrt{x^2}$

   G. $\frac{1}{2}\sqrt[3]{8x^3}$

   H. $\sqrt[3]{-x^3}$

   J. $\sqrt{x^2 + 2x + 1} - 1$

3. What is the real fourth root of $-\frac{16}{81}$?

   A. $\frac{2}{3}$

   B. $-\frac{2}{3}$

   C. $-\frac{4}{9}$

   D. no real fourth root

4. a is a number greater than 0. Which of the following is equal to $\sqrt{a^2(x + a^2)}$?

   F. $a\sqrt{x + a^2}$ **G.** $a\sqrt{x + a}$ **H.** $a\sqrt{x} + a$ **J.** $a(x^2 + a)$

5. What is the simplified form of the expression $\sqrt{4x^2y^4}$?

   A. $2xy^2$ **B.** $2|x|y^2$ **C.** $4xy^2$ **D.** $2|xy|$

6. Which of the following statements is true?

   F. x is always greater than $\sqrt{x}$.

   G. $x = \sqrt{x}$ only if $x = 0$.

   H. $\sqrt{\frac{1}{2}} > \frac{1}{2}$

   J. x^4 is always greater than x^2.

Short Response

7. The volume V of a cube with side length s is $V = s^3$. A cubical storage bin has volume 5832 cubic inches. What is the length of the side of the cube? Show your work.

SOLVE IT!

You can cut the 36-square into four 9-squares or nine 4-squares. What other *n*-square can you cut into sets of smaller squares in two ways? Is there a square you can cut into smaller squares in three ways? Explain your reasoning.

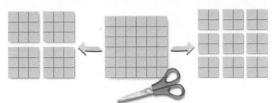

Interactive Exploration

Vocabulary Online

 Use Multiple Representations to Communicate Mathematical Ideas (1)(D)
What is another representation you could use to solve the problem? Explain why the representation would be useful.

TEKS Process Standard (1)(G)

 Problem 1 | **Got It?** | **Multiplying Radical Expressions**

Can you simplify the product of the radical expressions? Explain.

Learning Animation

a. $\sqrt[4]{7} \cdot \sqrt[5]{7}$

b. $\sqrt[5]{-5} \cdot \sqrt[5]{-2}$

 Problem 2 | **Got It?** | **Simplifying a Radical Expression**

What is the simplest form of $\sqrt[3]{128x^7}$?

Learning Animation

TEKS Process Standard (1)(D)

 Problem 3 | **Got It?** | **Simplifying a Product**

What is the simplest form of $\sqrt{45x^5y^3} \cdot \sqrt{35xy^4}$?

Learning Animation

Lesson 9-2 | Multiplying and Dividing Radical Expressions

Problem 4 | Got It? | Dividing Radical Expressions

Learning
Animation

a. What is the simplest form of $\dfrac{\sqrt{50x^6}}{\sqrt{2x^4}}$?

b. Can you simplify the expression in Part A of Problem 4 by first simplifying $\sqrt{18x^5}$ and $\sqrt{2x^3}$? Explain.

Problem 5 | Got It? | Rationalizing the Denominator

Learning
Animation

a. What is the simplest form of $\dfrac{\sqrt[3]{7x}}{\sqrt[3]{5y^2}}$?

b. Which choice in Problem 5 could be eliminated immediately? Explain your reasoning.

ELPS Discuss part (b) with a classmate. What does it mean to *eliminate* something *immediately*? What skills, definitions, and key concepts help you to quickly identify incorrect answer choices? Share your ideas with your classmate. Did your partner have helpful ideas that were different from yours?

Lesson 9-2 | Multiplying and Dividing Radical Expressions

Lesson Check

Do you know HOW?

1. Divide and simplify the expression $\dfrac{\sqrt[3]{48x^8}}{\sqrt[3]{3x^2}}$.

2. When the fourth root of an expression is written in simplest form, the result is $3x^2\sqrt[4]{6x}$. What is the original expression?

3. The formula $s = \dfrac{\sqrt[3]{m}}{\sqrt[3]{12}}$ relates the side length s of a cube, in centimeters, to its mass m, in grams, for the metal palladium. What is the simplest form of the right-hand side of the formula? Use the simplest form to find the side length of a cube of palladium with a mass of 324 grams.

Do you UNDERSTAND?

Math
Tools

Online
Practice

Virtual Nerd
Tutorials

4. Vocabulary Write the simplest form of $\sqrt[3]{32x^4}$.

5. Justify Mathematical Arguments (1)(G) For what values of x is $\sqrt{-4x^3}$ real? Justify your reasoning.

6. Explain Mathematical Ideas (1)(G) Explain the error in this simplification of radical expressions.

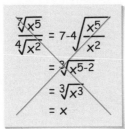

$$\frac{\sqrt[7]{x^5}}{\sqrt[4]{x^2}} = {}^{7-4}\!\sqrt{\frac{x^5}{x^2}}$$

$$= \sqrt[3]{x^{5-2}}$$

$$= \sqrt[3]{x^3}$$

$$= x$$

TEXAS Test Practice

Multiple Choice

For Exercises 1–5, choose the correct letter. Assume that all variables are positive.

1. What is the area of a triangle with base length $2\sqrt{7}$ and height $2\sqrt{2}$?

  A. $\sqrt{14}$ **B.** $\sqrt{28}$ **C.** $\sqrt{56}$ **D.** $\sqrt{112}$

2. What is the simplest form of $\sqrt{80x^7y^6}$?

  F. $2x^3y^3\sqrt{20x}$ **G.** $4x^6y^6\sqrt{5x^3}$ **H.** $4\sqrt{5x^7y^6}$ **J.** $4x^3y^3\sqrt{5x}$

3. What is the simplest form of $\sqrt[3]{25xy^2} \cdot \sqrt[3]{15x^2}$?

  A. $5x\sqrt[3]{3y^2}$ **B.** $5x\sqrt[3]{3y}$ **C.** $15xy\sqrt[3]{y}$ **D.** $5xy\sqrt{15x}$

4. Which of the following statements describes the equality $\sqrt{2a} = a\sqrt{2}$?

  F. It is never true for any value of a.

  G. It is true for only one value of a.

  H. It is true for only two values of a.

  J. It is valid for all values of a.

5. If $\sqrt{x^a} = x^{2b}$, then which of the following is true?

  A. $a = 2b$ **B.** $a = 4b$ **C.** $a = b$ **D.** $a = -b$

Short Response

6. The volume V of a wooden beam is $V = \ell s^2$, where ℓ is the length of the beam and s is the length of one side of its square cross section. If the volume of the beam is 1200 in.^{3} and its length is 96 in., what is the side length? Show your work.

SOLVE IT!

You are building right isosceles triangles around point O in the pattern shown. How many triangles must you build to completely encircle O? Explain your reasoning. What will be the area of the figure once you've made a full circle? What will be its perimeter?

Interactive Exploration

Vocabulary Online

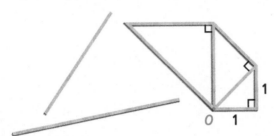

 Select Techniques to Solve Problems (1)(C) What other techniques could you use to solve the problem? Select one and explain how you would use it.

TEKS Process Standard (1)(G)

 Problem 1 **Got It?** **Adding and Subtracting Radical Expressions**

What is the simplified form of each expression?

a. $7\sqrt[3]{5} - 4\sqrt{5}$

b. $3x\sqrt{xy} + 4x\sqrt{xy}$

c. $17\sqrt[5]{3x^2} - 15\sqrt[5]{3x^2}$

Problem 2 | **Got It?** | **Using Radical Expressions**

Learning
Animation

a. Find the perimeter of the window in Problem 2 if the side of each small square is 6 in.

b. Describe a different sequence of steps that you could use to compute the perimeter of the window.

 ELPS Work with a classmate to solve the Got It. Then take turns describing the solution strategy using connecting words such as: *because, since, first, next, therefore, so, and, after, the main point, finally,* and *therefore.* When listening, help your partner rephrase any awkward statements.

TEKS Process Standard (1)(E)

 Problem 3 | **Got It?** | **Simplifying Before Adding or Subtracting**

What is the simplest form of the expression? $\sqrt[3]{250} + \sqrt[3]{54} - \sqrt[3]{16}$

Learning
Animation

Problem 4 | **Got It?** | Multiplying Binomial Radical Expressions

What is the product of $(3 + 2\sqrt{5})$ and $(2 + 4\sqrt{5})$?

Learning
Animation

Problem 5 | **Got It?** | Multiplying Conjugates

What is each product?

Learning
Animation

a. $(6 - \sqrt{12})(6 + \sqrt{12})$

b. $(3 + \sqrt{8})(3 - \sqrt{8})$

Problem 6 | **Got It?** | **Rationalizing the Denominator**

Learning
Animation

How can you write the expression with a rationalized denominator?

a. $\dfrac{2\sqrt{7}}{\sqrt{3} - \sqrt{5}}$

b. $\dfrac{4x}{3 - \sqrt{6}}$

c. Suppose you were going to rationalize the denominator of $\dfrac{1 - \sqrt{8}}{2 - \sqrt{8}}$. Would you simplify $\sqrt{8}$ before or after rationalizing? Explain your answer.

Lesson 9-3 | **Binomial Radical Expressions**

351

Lesson Check

Do you know HOW?

1. What is the product of $(5 + 2\sqrt{5})$ and $(7 + 4\sqrt{5})$?

Math
Tools

Online
Practice

Virtual Nerd
Tutorials

2. The product of $2 + \sqrt{3}$ and another binomial radical expression is $9 + 5\sqrt{3}$. What is the other binomial radical expression?

3. The perimeter of a square carpet is $8 + 12\sqrt{x}$ feet. What is the area of the carpet?

Do you UNDERSTAND?

4. Vocabulary Determine whether each of the following is a pair of like radicals. If so, add them.

a. $3x\sqrt{11}$ and $3x\sqrt{10}$

Math
Tools

Online
Practice

Virtual Nerd
Tutorials

b. $2\sqrt{3xy}$ and $7\sqrt{3xy}$

c. $12\sqrt{13y}$ and $12\sqrt{6y}$

5. Analyze Mathematic Relationships (1)(F) How are the processes of multiplying radical expressions and multiplying polynomial expressions alike? How are the processes different?

6. Explain Mathematical Ideas (1)(G) Show that the product of $n + \sqrt{n^2 - 1}$ and its conjugate $n - \sqrt{n^2 - 1}$ equals 1. Does the product of any two conjugates equal 1? Explain.

Multiple Choice

For Exercises 1–5, choose the correct letter.

1. In a square with side length s, the length of the square's diagonal is $s\sqrt{2}$. Which radical expression represents the sum of lengths of the diagonals of two squares with side lengths of $3\sqrt{3}$ and $4\sqrt{6}$?

   A. $5(3 + 4\sqrt{2})$ **C.** $\sqrt{5}(3 + 4\sqrt{2})$

   B. $6(3 + 4\sqrt{2})$ **D.** $\sqrt{6}(3 + 4\sqrt{2})$

2. The numbers a and b are identified on the number line below. What is the product ab, in simplest form?

   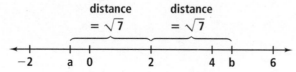

   distance $= \sqrt{7}$ distance $= \sqrt{7}$

   F. -3 **H.** -14

   G. $-12 - 3\sqrt{7}$ **J.** $3 + \sqrt{7}$

3. What is the simplified form of $\sqrt{2x^3y} \cdot 2\sqrt{2x^3y}$?

   A. $4\sqrt{x^3y}$

   B. $3\sqrt{2x^3y}$

   C. $4x^3y$

   D. This radical expression cannot be simplified further.

4. What is the simplest form of $\dfrac{7}{2 + \sqrt{5}}$?

   F. $-14 + 7\sqrt{5}$ **H.** $-14 - 7\sqrt{5}$

   G. $14 + 7\sqrt{5}$ **J.** $14 - 7\sqrt{5}$

5. What is the simplest form of $8\sqrt[3]{5} - \sqrt[3]{40} - 2\sqrt[3]{135}$?

   A. $16\sqrt[3]{5}$ **B.** $12\sqrt[3]{5}$ **C.** $4\sqrt[3]{5}$ **D.** 0

Short Response

6. A hiker drops a rock from the rim of the Grand Canyon. The distance it falls d in feet after t seconds is given by the function $d = 16t^2$. How far has the rock fallen after $(3 + \sqrt{2})$ seconds? Show your work.

9-4 Rational Exponents

 PearsonTEXAS.com

SOLVE IT!

Scan page for an interactive
version of this Solve It.

Based on the pattern in the table, what are the values of $9^{\frac{7}{2}}$ and $9^{\frac{9}{2}}$? Explain. Use your results and the laws of exponents to make a conjecture about the value of $9^{\frac{1}{2}}$.

x	$\frac{2}{2}$	$\frac{3}{2}$	$\frac{4}{2}$	$\frac{5}{2}$
9^x				

Interactive
Exploration

Vocabulary
Online

 Analyze Mathematical Relationships (1)(F) What mathematical relationships did you identify in the problem? How did you use them to solve the problem?

Lesson 9-4 | Rational Exponents

355

Copyright © by Pearson Education, Inc., or its affiliates. All Rights Reserved.

Problem 1 | Got It? | Simplifying Expressions With Rational Exponents

What is the simplified form of each expression?

a. $64^{\frac{1}{2}}$

b. $11^{\frac{1}{2}} \cdot 11^{\frac{1}{2}}$

c. $3^{\frac{1}{2}} \cdot 12^{\frac{1}{2}}$

Learning Animation

TEKS Process Standard (1)(D)

Problem 2 | Got It? | Converting Between Exponential and Radical Forms

a. What are the expressions $w^{-\frac{5}{8}}$ and $w^{0.2}$ in radical form?

b. What are the expressions $\sqrt[4]{x^3}$ and $(\sqrt[5]{y})^4$ in exponential form?

c. Refer to the definition of *rational exponent.* Explain the need for the restriction that $a \neq 0$ if m is negative.

Learning Animation

Problem 3 | **Got It?** | **Using Rational Exponents**

Find the approximate length (in Earth years) of each planet's year. Use the function $P = d^{\frac{3}{2}}$, where P is the number of Earth years it takes a planet to orbit the sun, and d is the distance from the sun in AU.

a. A Venusian year if Venus is 0.72 AU from the sun

b. A Jovian year if Jupiter is 5.46 AU from the sun

ELPS Listen as the instructor reads the Got It. With a partner, rewrite the question in your own words. Use a bilingual dictionary as needed. Include necessary information from Problem 3.

TEKS Process Standard (1)(E)

 Problem 4 Got It? **Combining Radical Expressions**

What is each product or quotient in simplest form?

a. $\sqrt{3}(\sqrt[4]{3})$

b. $\dfrac{\sqrt{x^3}}{\sqrt[3]{x^2}}$

c. $\sqrt{7}(\sqrt[3]{7})$

Learning Animation

Problem 5 Got It? **Simplifying Numbers with Rational Exponents**

What is each number in simplest form?

a. $32^{-\frac{3}{5}}$

b. $16^{\frac{3}{4}}$

c. $9^{-3.5}$

Learning Animation

Problem 6 | **Got It?** | Writing Expressions in Simplest Form

Learning Animation

What is each expression in simplest form?

a. $(8x^{15})^{-\frac{1}{3}}$

b. $(9x\sqrt[4]{y})^{\frac{3}{2}}$

Lesson 9-4 | Rational Exponents

359

Lesson Check

Do you know HOW?

1. Simplify the expression $\dfrac{\sqrt[3]{x}}{\sqrt[6]{x^5}}$.

Math
Tools

Online
Practice

Virtual Nerd
Tutorials

2. What value of x makes the following equation true?

$$2^{\frac{3}{4}} \cdot 2^{x} = 4$$

3. A scientist developed the equation $t = \dfrac{2w^{\frac{2}{3}}}{3}$ to find the cooking time for a stuffed turkey. In the equation, t is the time in hours and w is the weight of the turkey in pounds. To the nearest pound, what is the weight of the heaviest stuffed turkey that you can cook in less than 4 hours?

Do you UNDERSTAND?

Math
Tools

Online
Practice

Virtual Nerd
Tutorials

4. Explain Mathematical Ideas (1)(G) Explain why $(-64)^{\frac{1}{3}} = -64^{\frac{1}{3}}$ but $(-64)^{\frac{1}{2}} \neq -64^{\frac{1}{2}}$.

5. Explain Mathematical Ideas (1)(G) Explain why this simplification is incorrect.

$$5(4 - 5^{\frac{1}{2}})$$
$$5(4) - 5(5^{\frac{1}{2}})$$
$$20 - 25^{\frac{1}{2}}$$
$$15$$

6. Analyze Mathematical Relationships (1)(F) Find a nonzero number q such that $q(1 - 2^{\frac{1}{2}})$ is a rational number. Explain.

Lesson 9-4 | Rational Exponents

361

TEXAS Test Practice

Multiple Choice

For Exercises 1–5, choose the correct letter.

1. The volume of a sphere with radius r is given by $V = \frac{4}{3}\pi r^3$. The height of a cube of volume v is given by $h = v^{\frac{1}{3}}$. A cube has the same volume as a sphere of radius r. What is the height of the cube, in terms of r?

   A. $\left(\frac{4}{3}\pi r\right)^{\frac{1}{3}}$　　　**B.** $\frac{4}{3}\pi r$　　　**C.** $\left(\frac{4}{3}\pi\right)^{\frac{1}{3}}r$　　　**D.** $\frac{4}{9}\pi r$

2. What is $\left(\dfrac{x^{\frac{2}{3}}y^{\frac{1}{3}}}{x^{\frac{1}{2}}y^{\frac{3}{4}}}\right)^6$ in simplest form?

   F. $xy^{\frac{5}{2}}$　　　**G.** $x^7y^{\frac{5}{2}}$　　　**H.** $\dfrac{1}{xy^{\frac{5}{2}}}$　　　**J.** $\dfrac{x}{y^{\frac{5}{2}}}$

3. What is the result of rewriting the expression $(-32x^{10}y^{35})^{-\frac{1}{5}}$ so that it does not contain any negative or fractional exponents?

   A. $2x^2y^7$　　　**B.** $-\dfrac{2}{x^2y^7}$　　　**C.** $-\dfrac{1}{2x^2y^7}$　　　**D.** $\dfrac{2}{x^2y^7}$

4. What is the x-intercept of the function $y = 2^{\frac{1}{3}+x} - 4$?

   F. $\left(-\frac{5}{3}, 0\right)$　　　**G.** $\left(\frac{1}{3}, 0\right)$　　　**H.** $\left(\frac{5}{3}, 0\right)$　　　**J.** $(4, 0)$

5. What is $12^{\frac{1}{3}} \cdot 45^{\frac{1}{3}} \cdot 50^{\frac{1}{3}}$ in simplest form?

   A. $\sqrt{27{,}000}$　　　**B.** 30　　　**C.** $107^{\frac{1}{3}}$　　　**D.** 27,000

Short Response

6. The surface area S, in square units, of a sphere with volume V, in cubic units, is given by the formula $S = \pi^{\frac{1}{3}}(6V)^{\frac{2}{3}}$. What is the surface area of a sphere with volume $\frac{4}{3}$ mi^3? Show your work.

PearsonTEXAS.com

 **SOLVE IT!**

Scan page for an interactive version of this Solve It.

The graph of the parent cubic function $f(x) = x^3$ is shown at the right. The other graphs are transformations of the parent function. Which equation goes with which graph? How do you know?

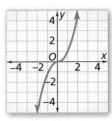

Interactive Exploration

Vocabulary Online

| $f(x) = (x - 3)^3 + 2$ | $f(x) = (x + 3)^3 - 2$ | $f(x) = -x^3$ |

| $f(x) = (x - 2)^3 + 3$ | $f(x) = x^3$ | $f(x) = (x + 2)^3 - 3$ |

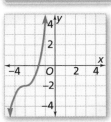      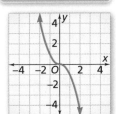

 Connect Mathematical Ideas (1)(F) What prior knowledge did you draw on to solve the problem?

Problem 1 | **Got It?** | Analyzing the Key Attributes of the Cubic Parent Function

Learning Animation

What are the minimum and maximum values of the function $f(x) = x^3$ on the interval $[-4, -2]$?

 Problem 2 | **Got It?** | Analyzing $y = f(x) + d$ for $f(x) = x^3$

Learning Animation

Graph each function on the same set of axes as the parent function $f(x) = x^3$. How does each y-intercept change under the transformation?

a. $y = x^3 + 27$

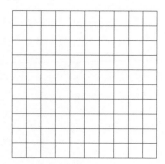

b. $y = x^3 - 1$

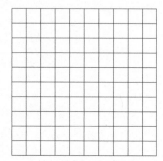

Lesson 10-1 | Attributes and Transformations of Cubic Functions

Problem 3 | **Got It?** | Analyzing $y = f(x - c)$ for $f(x) = x^3$

Learning
Animation

Graph each function on the same set of axes as the parent function $f(x) = x^3$. How do the intercepts change under the transformation?

a. $y = (x + 3)^3$

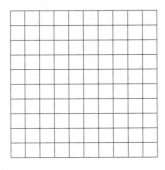

b. $y = (x - 1)^3$

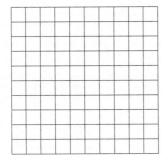

Problem 4 | **Got It?** | Analyzing $y = af(x)$ for $f(x) = x^3$

Graph each function on the same set of axes as the parent function $f(x) = x^3$.
How does the symmetry change under each transformation?

Learning Animation

a. $y = -2x^3$

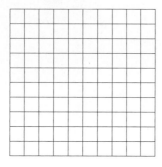

b. $y = 3x^3$

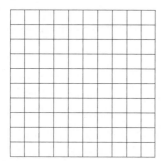

Problem 5 Got It? Analyzing $y = f(bx)$ for $f(x) = x^3$

Graph each function on the same set of axes as the parent function $f(x) = x^3$. How does the symmetry change under each transformation?

Learning Animation

a. $y = (4x)^3$

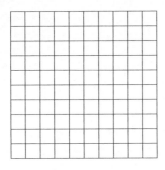

b. $y = \left(-\frac{1}{4}x\right)^3$

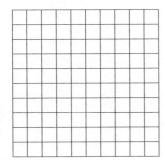

TEKS Process Standard (1)(A)

 Problem 6 Got It? **Modeling With a Cubic Function**

The power P (in kilowatts) generated by a wind turbine varies directly as the cube of the wind speed v (in meters per second). A turbine generates 210 kW of power in a 12 m/s wind. How much power does this turbine generate in a 20 m/s wind?

 Learning Animation

ELPS Make two lists of words you read in Problem 6 and the Got It, one for words you know, and another for words you do not understand. Share what you know with classmates, and ask for clarification of words you did not understand.

Lesson Check

Do you know HOW?

1. Graph $y = (x - 3)^3 + 1$ on the same set of axes as its parent function $f(x) = x^3$.

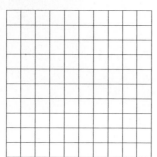

Math Tools

Online Practice

Virtual Nerd Tutorials

2. The graph shows a function that is a transformation of $f(x) = x^3$. Identify the function.

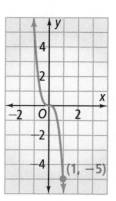

3. The volume V of a balloon varies directly with the cube of its radius r. If the volume is 113 cubic inches when the radius is 3 inches, find the formula for the volume.

Lesson Check

Do you UNDERSTAND?

Math
Tools

Online
Practice

Virtual Nerd
Tutorials

4. Vocabulary Why is the term *cubic* appropriate for a polynomial function of degree three?

5. Analyze Mathematical Relationships (1)(F) Let a be a nonzero real number. Which of the functions below passes through the origin? Explain your reasoning.

$$f(x) = (x - a)^3 \qquad g(x) = x^3 - a \qquad h(x) = ax^3$$

6. Justify Mathematical Arguments (1)(G) Justify the argument that the equation $b = (x - a)^3$ has a solution for x, regardless of the values of real numbers a and b.

Lesson 10-1 | **Attributes and Transformations of Cubic Functions**

TEXAS Test Practice

Multiple Choice

For Exercises 1–4, choose the correct letter.

1. The graph of which function is a translation of the graph of $f(x) = x^3$ down 2 units and right 5 units?

A. $g(x) = (x + 2)^3 - 5$ **C.** $g(x) = (x + 5)^3 - 2$

B. $g(x) = (x - 2)^3 + 5$ **D.** $g(x) = (x - 5)^3 - 2$

2. For which function $f(x)$ does $f(-100)$ have the greatest value?

F. $f(x) = x^3 + 20$ **H.** $f(x) = (x + 20)^3$

G. $f(x) = -0.1x^3$ **J.** $f(x) = (0.1x)^3$

3. The graph at the right shows two functions. One function is $f(x) = x^3$, and the second function is a transformation of the first. What is the second function?

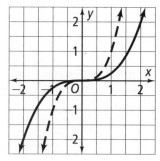

A. $g(x) = \frac{1}{4}x^3$

B. $g(x) = 4x^3 - 4$

C. $g(x) = -4x^3$

D. $g(x) = -4x^2$

4. Which transformation maps $f(x) = (x - 10)^3$ to $g(x) = (x - 10)^3 + 2$?

F. a translation left 2 units

G. a translation up 2 units

H. a compression by a factor of $\frac{1}{10}$

J. a reflection across the line $x = 10$

Short Response

5. Describe the transformations that map $f(x) = x^3$ to $g(x) = 0.5x^3 - 3$.

SOLVE IT!

Suppose the volume of a cylinder is between 16π cubic units and 250π cubic units, inclusive. The height of the cylinder is two times the radius. What are the possible minimum and maximum radius and height of the cylinder? (*Hint:* The formula for the volume of a cylinder is $V = \pi r^2 h$.)

Interactive
Exploration

Vocabulary
Online

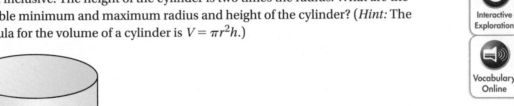

Use a Problem-Solving Model (1)(B) Evaluate your problem-solving model. Which parts were helpful? Which would you want to revise? Explain.

 **Problem 1** **Got It?** Analyzing the Key Attributes of
Cube Root Functions

Learning
Animation

Graph each cube root function and analyze the domain, range, intercepts,
and symmetry.

a. $f(x) = \sqrt[3]{x} - 2$

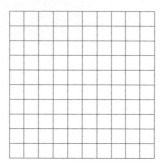

b. $f(x) = \sqrt[3]{x - 1}$

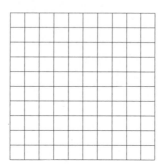

ELPS Read the Got It and discuss the term *analyze* with a classmate. How does a
close examination of the graph help you find the *domain, range, symmetry,* and
intercepts?

TEKS Process Standard (1)(D)

 Problem 2 | **Got It?** | Finding the Maximums and Minimums of Cube Root Functions

 Learning Animation

Graph each cube root function. What are the minimum and the maximum on the given interval?

a. $f(x) = \sqrt[3]{x} + 1;\ [-8, 0]$

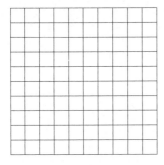

b. $f(x) = \sqrt[3]{x + 2};\ [-2, 6]$

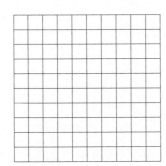

 Problem 3 | **Got It?** | Interpreting Attributes of a Cube Root Function

In Problem 3, the function $y = \sqrt[3]{x}$ modeled the length y of an edge of a cube, in inches, when the volume of the cube was x cubic inches. Your graph from Problem 3 is shown at the right. Interpret the minimum and maximum values of the function on the interval $[27, 64]$.

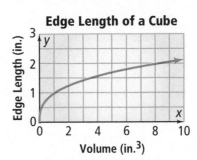

Edge Length of a Cube

 Learning Animation

Problem 4 Got It? **Writing and Graphing the Inverse of $f(x)$**

What is the inverse of the cubic function $f(x) = \frac{1}{2}(x + 2)^3$? Graph $f(x)$ and $f^{-1}(x)$ and describe the relationship between the functions.

 Learning Animation

Problem 5 Got It? Proving a Cubic and Cube Root Function
Are Inverses

Learning
Animation

Use composition of functions to determine whether $f(x) = (4x)^3$ and $g(x) = \sqrt[3]{\frac{x}{4}}$
are inverses. Explain.

Lesson Check

Do you know HOW?

1. Graph the function $y = \sqrt[3]{(x+8)}$. Identify the domain, range, x-intercept, and y-intercept of the function.

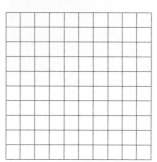

Math Tools

Online Practice

Virtual Nerd Tutorials

2. Let $f(x) = -8(x-1)^3 + 2$. Find $f^{-1}(x)$. How many x-intercepts does $f^{-1}(x)$ have? How do you know?

3. The function $f(x)$ is a cube root function that has rotational symmetry about the point $(2, 0)$. Complete the table and identify $f(x)$.

x	−25	−6	1	2	3	10	29
f(x)			−3	0		6	

Do you UNDERSTAND?

Math Tools

Online Practice

Virtual Nerd Tutorials

4. Vocabulary How is a *cube root function* related to a *cubic function*?

5. Analyze Mathematical Relationships (1)(F) Let $f(x) = \sqrt[3]{x - a}$, where a is a nonzero real number. What are the domain and range of $f(x)$? Does the function have a horizontal or vertical asymptote? Explain.

6. Explain Mathematical Ideas (1)(G) Let $f(x) = \sqrt[3]{x}$; $g(x) = \sqrt[3]{x} + 9$; and $h(x) = \sqrt[3]{x} + 99$. How do the ranges of the three functions compare?

TEXAS Test Practice

Multiple Choice

For Exercises 1–4, choose the correct letter.

1. The function $s = 3.7\sqrt[3]{p}$ models the speed s of a bicycle, in miles per hour, when the cyclist's power output is p watts. If the cyclist doubles her power output, by what factor does her speed increase?

  A. $\sqrt[3]{2}$ **C.** 4

  B. 2   **D.** 8

2. What is the maximum value of the function $f(x) = \sqrt[3]{\frac{2x}{3}} + 8$ over the interval $[-1, 1]$?

  F. $f(-1)$ **H.** $f(0)$

  G. $f\left(\frac{1}{2}\right)$ **J.** $f(1)$

3. The graph of $f(x) = \sqrt[3]{x-3} + 7$ has rotational symmetry about which of the following points?

  A. $(0, \sqrt[3]{-3} + 7)$ **C.** $(3, 7)$

  B. $(4, 8)$ **D.** $(-340, 0)$

4. Which function $g(x)$ is the inverse of $f(x) = 2(x+4)^3$?

  F. $g(x) = \sqrt[3]{\frac{x}{2}} - 4$ **H.** $g(x) = \sqrt[3]{\frac{x-4}{2}}$

  G. $g(x) = \sqrt[3]{\frac{2x-1}{4}}$ **J.** $g(x) = \frac{1}{2}\sqrt[3]{x} + 4$

Short Response

5. Use composition of functions to show that $f(x) = x^3 - 6$ and $g(x) = \sqrt[3]{x+6}$ are inverses of each other.

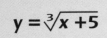 **SOLVE IT!**

Use technology to graph the following cube root functions. How are they similar? How are they different?

$$y = \sqrt[3]{x} + 5$$

$$y = \sqrt[3]{x} + 5$$

$$y = 5\sqrt[3]{x}$$

$$y = \sqrt[3]{5x}$$

Interactive Exploration

Vocabulary Online

 Select Techniques to Solve Problems (1)(C) What other techniques could you use to solve the problem? Select one and explain how you would use it.

Problem 1 | **Got It?** | Analyzing $y = f(x) + d$ for $f(x) = \sqrt[3]{x}$

 Learning Animation

Graph the functions $g(x) = \sqrt[3]{x} + 3$ and $h(x) = \sqrt[3]{x} - 3$ on the same set of axes as the parent function $f(x) = \sqrt[3]{x}$.

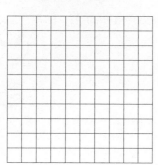

ELPS Discuss vertical translations of cube root functions with a classmate. Take turns summarizing facts. Correct language errors as you speak, saying things such as: Let me rephrase ___. I meant to say ___. A better way to say this is ___.

 Problem 2 | **Got It?** | Analyzing $y = f(x - c)$ for $f(x) = \sqrt[3]{x}$

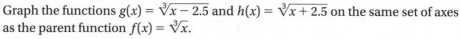 Learning Animation

Graph the functions $g(x) = \sqrt[3]{x - 2.5}$ and $h(x) = \sqrt[3]{x + 2.5}$ on the same set of axes as the parent function $f(x) = \sqrt[3]{x}$.

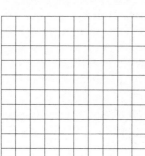

Problem 3 | **Got It?** | Analyzing $y = af(x)$ for $f(x) = \sqrt[3]{x}$

Graph the given functions on the same set of axes as the parent function $f(x) = \sqrt[3]{x}$.

a. $g(x) = 4\sqrt[3]{x}$, $h(x) = -4\sqrt[3]{x}$

b. $g(x) = 0.5\sqrt[3]{x}$, $h(x) = -0.5\sqrt[3]{x}$

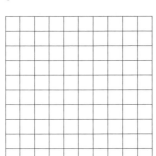

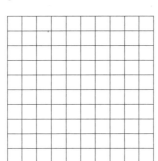

Problem 4 | **Got It?** | Analyzing $y = f(bx)$ for $f(x) = \sqrt[3]{x}$

Graph the given functions on the same set of axes as the parent function $f(x) = \sqrt[3]{x}$.

a. $g(x) = \sqrt[3]{\frac{1}{3}x}$, $h(x) = \sqrt[3]{-\frac{1}{3}x}$

b. $g(x) = \sqrt[3]{2x}$, $h(x) = \sqrt[3]{-2x}$

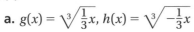

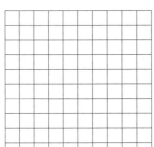

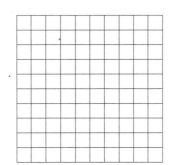

TEKS Process Standard (1)(F)

Problem 5 | **Got It?** | Graphing a Cube Root Function

The function $y = 3 - \frac{1}{2}\sqrt[3]{x - 2}$ models the population y of a city, in millions, x years after 2000. What is the graph of the function?

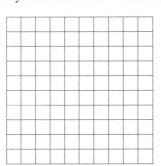

Lesson 10-3 | Transformations of Cube Root Functions

Lesson Check

Do you know HOW?

1. Graph the parent function $y = \sqrt[3]{x}$ and the function $y = \sqrt[3]{(x + 2)} - 5$. What transformation maps the parent function to the second function?

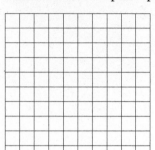

Math Tools

Online Practice

Virtual Nerd Tutorials

2. The graph shows a function that is a transformation of $y = \sqrt[3]{x}$ and includes the point $(8, -8)$. Identify the function.

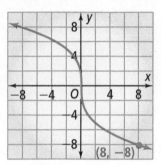

3. The function $V(x) = 0.9\sqrt[3]{x - 3} + 2$ models the value $V(x)$ of an investment, in thousands of dollars, after x years. Describe the transformation that maps the parent function $y = \sqrt[3]{x}$ to $V(x)$.

Do you UNDERSTAND?

4. Analyze Mathematical Relationships (1)(F) Let a be a nonzero real number. What is the relationship between the graphs of $f(x) = a\sqrt[3]{x}$ and $g(x) = -a\sqrt[3]{x}$?

Math
Tools

Online
Practice

Virtual Nerd
Tutorials

5. Analyze Mathematical Relationships (1)(F) Let $f(x) = a\sqrt[3]{x}$, in which a is a nonzero real number. What is the domain and range of $f(x)$? Does the function have a horizontal or vertical asymptote? Explain.

6. Justify Mathematical Arguments (1)(G) Your classmate claimed that the point $(1, 4)$ lies on several different transformations of the function $y = \sqrt[3]{x}$. Use examples of translations, stretches, and compressions to justify your classmate's argument.

TEXAS Test Practice

Multiple Choice

For Exercises 1–4, choose the correct letter.

1. The graph of which function $g(x)$ is a translation of the graph of $f(x) = \sqrt[3]{x}$ up 1.8 units and right 3.3 units?

A. $g(x) = 3.3\sqrt[3]{x} + 1.8$

C. $g(x) = \sqrt[3]{(x - 1.8)} + 3.3$

B. $g(x) = \sqrt[3]{(x - 3.3)} + 1.8$

D. $g(x) = \sqrt[3]{(x + 3.3)} + 1.8$

2. The graph of which function $f(x)$ passes through the point $(-8, -1)$ and is a vertical compression of the parent function $y = \sqrt[3]{x}$?

F. $f(x) = 0.5\sqrt[3]{x}$

H. $f(x) = \sqrt[3]{x} + 1$

G. $f(x) = 8\sqrt[3]{x}$

J. $f(x) = 0.75\sqrt[3]{x} + 7$

3. The graph shows two functions: $y = \sqrt[3]{x}$ and a second function that is a transformation of the first. What is the second function?

A. $y = -\sqrt[3]{x} + 6$

B. $y = -\sqrt[3]{x + 6}$

C. $y = -\sqrt[3]{x - 6}$

D. $y = -6\sqrt[3]{x} + 6$

4. Which transformation maps the graph of $f(x) = \sqrt[3]{(x - 8)}$ to the graph of $g(x) = 4\sqrt[3]{(x - 8)}$?

F. a translation of 8 to the right

G. a translation of 4 to the right

H. a vertical compression by a factor of $\frac{1}{8}$

J. a vertical stretch by a factor of 4

Short Response

5. Describe the transformation that maps the graph of $f(x) = \sqrt[3]{x}$ to the graph of $g(x) = 0.5\sqrt[3]{x} + 3$.

10-4 Cube Root Equations

SOLVE IT!

A warehouse worker stacks identical cube-shaped boxes inside a 512 cubic-foot storage container. There are 2 ft of empty space to the right of, in front of, and above the boxes. What are the dimensions of each box? How many more boxes could fit in the space?

Front view

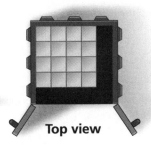

Top view

 Use Multiple Representations to Communicate Mathematical Ideas (1)(D)
What is another representation you could use to solve the problem? Explain why the representation would be useful.

TEKS Process Standard (1)(B)

 Problem 1 | **Got It?** | **Solving a Cube Root Equation With Real Roots**

What is the solution of the equation $5 = \sqrt[3]{7x + 6}$? Evaluate your
problem-solving process.

Learning Animation

 Problem 2 | **Got It?** | **Solving Equations With Rational Exponents**

What are the solutions of $2(x + 3)^{\frac{2}{3}} = 8$?

Learning Animation

ELPS Discuss methods for solving radical equations with a classmate and write a step-by-step procedure together. Ask your partner to rephrase statements that you do not fully understand, or use sentence stems such as: What I heard you say was ___.

Problem 3 **Got It?** Using a Cube Root Equation

Learning
Animation

The formula $d = 2\sqrt[3]{\dfrac{V}{0.3}}$ relates the diameter d of a crater's rim (in meters) to its volume V (in cubic meters). Suppose a crater has a diameter of 1 km. What is the volume of the crater?

 Problem 4 **Got It?** Solving a Cube Root Equation by Graphing

Learning
Animation

You can model the population P of Corpus Christi, Texas, between the years 1970 and 2005 by the cube root function $P(x) = 75{,}000 \sqrt[3]{x - 1950}$, where x is the year. Using this model, in what year was the population of Corpus Christi 275,000?

Lesson Check

Do you know HOW?

1. Solve for x.

$$\sqrt[3]{4x - 13} - 1 = 2$$

Math Tools

Online Practice

Virtual Nerd Tutorials

2. Solve for x.

$$\sqrt[3]{x^3 + 28} = 3$$

3. The cube root of a number is $\frac{1}{5}$ times the cube root of 4 more than the number. What is the number?

Do you UNDERSTAND?

Math Tools

Online Practice

Virtual Nerd Tutorials

4. Use Multiple Representations to Communicate Mathematical Ideas (1)(D)
Describe two ways of solving a cube root equation. Use $5 = \sqrt[3]{2x - 1}$ as an example.

5. Connect Mathematical Ideas (1)(F) How is solving a cube root equation similar to solving a square root equation? How is it different?

6. Explain Mathematical Ideas (1)(G) For polynomial functions $f(x)$ and $g(x)$, does the equation $f(x) = g(x)$ have the same solution as the equation $\sqrt[3]{f(x)} = \sqrt[3]{g(x)}$? Choose a specific example to include in your explanation.

TEXAS Test Practice

Gridded Response

Solve each exercise and enter your answer in the grid provided.

1. The volume of a spherical water tank is given by $V = \frac{d^3\pi}{6}$, where d is the diameter of the tank. If the tank can hold 3000 ft^3 of water, what is its diameter, in feet? Round your answer to two decimal places.

2. What is the solution? $5x^{\frac{1}{3}} - 8 = 7$

3. What is the solution? $\sqrt[3]{2x - 6} = \sqrt[3]{3 - x}$

4. What is the solution? $\sqrt[3]{\sqrt[3]{\sqrt[3]{x - 9}}} = 1$

1. 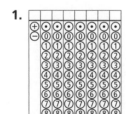 **2.** 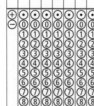 **3.** 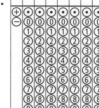 **4.**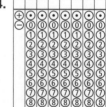

SOLVE IT!

You have 20 bags of mulch. You plan to spread the mulch from all the bags to make a rectangular layer that is 3 in. thick. How many square feet can you cover? If ℓ and w represent the length and width of the rectangle in feet, what equation relates ℓ and w? Justify your reasoning.

Interactive Exploration

Vocabulary Online

 Explain Mathematical Ideas (1)(G) A classmate questions your solution to the problem. Use precise mathematical language to explain why your solution is correct.

TEKS Process Standard (1)(D)

 Problem 1 | **Got It?** | **Identifying Direct and Inverse Variations**

Learning Animation

Is the relationship between the variables a *direct variation,* an *inverse variation,* or *neither*? Write function models for the direct and inverse variations.

a.

x	y
0.2	8
0.5	20
1.0	40
1.5	60

b.

x	y
0.2	40
0.5	16
1.0	8.0
2.0	4.0

c.

x	y
0.5	40
1.2	12
2	10
2.5	6

 Problem 2 | **Got It?** | **Determining an Inverse Variation**

Learning Animation

Suppose x and y vary inversely, and $x = 8$ when $y = -7$.

a. What is the function that models the inverse variation?

b. What does the graph of this function look like?

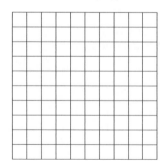

c. What is y when $x = 2$?

Problem 3 | **Got It?** | **Modeling an Inverse Variation**

After a major storm, your math class volunteers to remove debris from yards. The table shows the time *t* in minutes that it takes a group of *n* students to remove the debris from an average-sized yard.

Learning Animation

Number of students (*n*)	1	3	5	14
Time in minutes (*t*)	225	75	45	16

a. What function models the time needed to clear the debris from an average-sized yard relative to the number of students who do the work?

b. How many students should there be to clear debris from an average-sized yard in at most 25 minutes?

Problem 4 **Got It?** **Using Combined Variation**

The number of bags of mulch you need to cover a planting area varies jointly with the area to be mulched a in square feet and the depth of the mulch d in feet. If you need 10 bags to mulch 120 ft^2 to a depth of 3 in., how many bags do you need to mulch 200 ft^2 to a depth of 4 in.?

Learning Animation

Lesson 11-1 | **Inverse Variation**

394

Problem 5 **Got It?** Applying Combined Variation

Learning
Animation

Use the potential energy formula $PE = 9.8mh$ from Problem 5.

a. How much potential energy would a 41-kg diver have standing on a 10-m diving platform?

b. An 80-kg diver stands on a 6-m diving platform. At what height should a 40-kg diver stand to have equal potential energy? Do you need to find the potential energy of either diver to solve this? Explain.

 Read part (a) with a classmate. Draw a diagram of a diver on a platform to use as visual support. Which part of your diagram represents height? Mass? What vocabulary words are represented by PE, m, and h in the formula $PE = 9.8mh$? How does the context of a diving problem help you understand the formula for potential energy?

Do you know HOW?

1. Determine whether the relationship between the variables in the table is a *direct variation*, an *inverse variation*, or *neither*. Write an equation to model direct or inverse variation.

x	y
1	6
3	2
12	0.5
15	0.4

Math Tools

Online Practice

Virtual Nerd Tutorials

2. Assume $p \neq 0$. Determine whether the relationship between the variables in the table is a *direct variation*, an *inverse variation*, or *neither*. Write an equation to model direct or inverse variation.

x	y
12p	3p
4p	p
2p	$\frac{p}{2}$
$\frac{p}{6}$	$\frac{p}{24}$

3. The maximum weight m that can be supported by a wooden board varies jointly with its width w and the square of its thickness h, and inversely with its length ℓ. Describe four ways the board can be modified to quadruple the maximum weight the board can support.

Lesson Check

Math Tools

Online Practice

Virtual Nerd Tutorials

Do you UNDERSTAND?

4. Vocabulary Describe the difference between direct variation and inverse variation.

5. Analyze Mathematical Relationships (1)(F) Suppose c varies inversely with d, and d varies inversely with w. Describe the relationship between c and w. Explain your reasoning.

6. Use Representations to Communicate Mathematical Ideas (1)(E)
A student says that in the equation $d = \dfrac{k\sqrt[3]{r}}{t^2}$, d varies directly with r and inversely with t. Correct the error in describing the relationship among the variables.

TEXAS Test Practice

Multiple Choice

For Exercises 1–5, choose the correct letter.

1. The number of bags of mulch b that a gardener needs to cover a garden depends on the area a of the garden and the depth d of mulch. Which of the following equations models the relationship between these variables?

   A. $b = kad$ **B.** $k = \frac{da}{b}$ **C.** $d = kba$ **D.** $bda = k$

2. The ordered pair $(3.5, 1.2)$ is from an inverse variation. What is the constant of variation?

   F. 2.3   **G.** 2.9   **H.** 4.2   **J.** 4.7

3. Suppose x and y vary inversely, and $x = 4$ when $y = 9$. Which function models the inverse variation?

   A. $y = \frac{36}{x}$ **B.** $x = \frac{y}{36}$ **C.** $y = \frac{x}{36}$ **D.** $\frac{x}{y} = 36$

4. Suppose x and y vary inversely, and $x = -3$ when $y = \frac{1}{3}$. What is the value of y when $x = 9$?

   F. -9 **G.** -1 **H.** $-\frac{1}{9}$ **J.** $\frac{1}{9}$

5. In which function does t vary jointly with q and r and inversely with s?

   A. $t = \frac{kq}{rs}$ **B.** $t = \frac{ks}{qr}$ **C.** $t = \frac{s}{kqr}$ **D.** $t = \frac{kqr}{s}$

Short Response

6. A student suggests that the graph at the right represents the inverse variation $y = \frac{3}{x}$. Is the student correct? Explain.

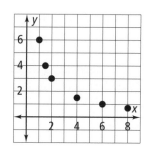

SOLVE IT!

For a class party, the students will share the cost for the hall rental. Each student will also have to pay $8 for food. The cost of the hall rental is already graphed. What effect does the food cost have on the graph? Explain your reasoning.

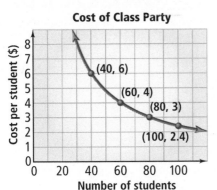

Cost of Class Party

(40, 6)
(60, 4)
(80, 3)
(100, 2.4)

Cost per student ($)

Number of students

Interactive Exploration

Vocabulary Online

 Use Multiple Representations to Communicate Mathematical Ideas (1)(D)
What is another representation you could use to present your solution? Explain how the representation communicates the same information.

TEKS Process Standard (1)(E)

 Problem 1 | **Got It?** | **Graphing an Inverse Variation Function**

Learning
Animation

a. What is the graph of $y = \frac{12}{x}$? Identify the x- and y-intercepts and the asymptotes of the graph. Also, state the domain and range of the function in interval notation.

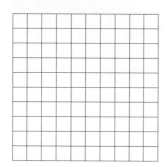

b. Would the function $y = \frac{6}{x}$ have the same domain and range as $y = \frac{8}{x}$ or $y = \frac{12}{x}$? Explain.

 Problem 2 | **Got It?** | **Analyzing the Graph of** $af(x)$ **When** $f(x) = \frac{1}{x}$

Learning
Animation

For each given value of a, how do the graphs of $y = \frac{1}{x}$ and $y = \frac{a}{x}$ compare? What is the effect of a on the graph?

a. $a = \frac{1}{2}$

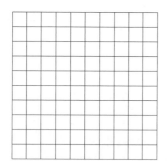

b. $a = 2$

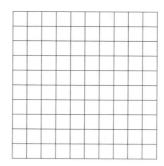

c. $a = -\frac{1}{2}$

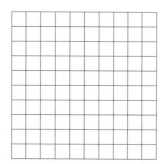

Problem 3 **Got It?** Analyzing the Graph of $f(x) + d$ When $f(x) = \frac{1}{x}$

Learning Animation

What is the graph of each rational function? How is each graph different from the parent function $f(x) = \frac{1}{x}$?

a. $y = \frac{1}{x} - 1$

b. $y = \frac{1}{x} + 4$

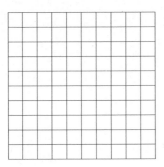

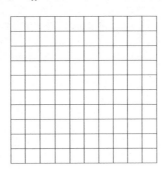

 Problem 4 **Got It?** Analyzing the Graph of $f(x - c)$ When $f(x) = \frac{1}{x}$

Learning Animation

What is the graph of each function? How do the domain and range of each function compare to the domain and range of the parent function $f(x) = \frac{1}{x}$?

a. $y = \frac{1}{x - 4}$

b. $y = \frac{1}{x + 6}$

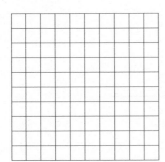

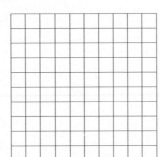

Problem 5 **Got It?** Analyzing the Graph of $f(bx)$ When $f(x) = \frac{1}{x}$

Learning Animation

a. Sketch the graphs of the functions $f(x) = \frac{1}{x}$, $g(x) = \frac{1}{10x}$, and $h(x) = -\frac{1}{4x}$ on the same set of axes.

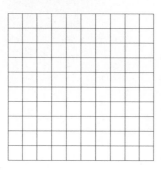

b. Determine the effects on the graph of the parent function $f(x)$ for the functions $g(x)$ and $h(x)$.

Problem 6 | **Got It?** | Writing the Equation of a Transformation

This graph of a function is a translation of the graph of $y = \frac{2}{x}$. What is an equation for the function?

Learning
Animation

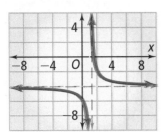

TEKS Process Standard (1)(C)

 Problem 7 | **Got It?** | Using a Reciprocal Function

The junior class is renting a laser tag facility with a capacity of 325 people. The cost for the facility is $1200. The party must have 13 adult chaperones.

Learning
Animation

a. If every student who attends shares the facility cost equally, what function models the cost per student C with respect to the number of students n who attend? What is the domain of the function? How many students must attend to make the cost per student no more than $7.50?

b. The class wants to promote the event by giving away 30 spots to students in a drawing. How does the model change? Now how many paying students must attend so the cost for each is no more than $7.50?

 Make a Know/Need/Plan graphic organizer. Then read part (a) with a classmate. Fill in the following information as you read. What is the capacity of the facility? How much does it cost to use the facility? How many people will not have to pay to attend? What is the maximum amount each student should pay to attend?

Lesson Check

Do you know HOW?

1. What are the asymptotes of the graph of $y = \frac{5}{x + 2} - 7$?

Math
Tools

Online
Practice

Virtual Nerd
Tutorials

2. Sketch the graph of $xy + 4 = 0$. Describe the transformation from the graph of $y = \frac{1}{x}$ to the graph of this function.

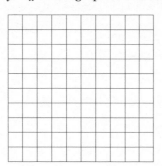

3. A school is considering renting out a room for a school dance. The cost to rent it is $400. What function models the cost per student attending? What does the function change to if the room is rented at a 25% discount and 10 of the students attending win free tickets to the dance in a contest?

Do you UNDERSTAND?

4. Vocabulary Are all members of the reciprocal function family inverse variation functions?

Math Tools

Online Practice

Virtual Nerd Tutorials

5. Create Representations to Communicate Mathematical Ideas (1)(E)
Write an equation of a stretch and a reflection of the graph of $y = \frac{1}{x}$ across the x-axis.

6. Use Representations to Communicate Mathematical Ideas (1)(E)
Explain how you can tell if a function $y = \frac{a}{x}$ is a stretch or a compression of the parent function $y = \frac{1}{x}$.

TEXAS Test Practice

Multiple Choice

For Exercises 1–3, choose the correct letter.

1. The time t it takes to travel a distance d is proportional to the product of the distance traveled and the reciprocal of the speed s of travel. Which of the following equations represents this relationship?

   A. $t = \dfrac{s}{d}$ **C.** $t = sd$

   B. $t = \dfrac{d}{s}$ **D.** $t = d - s$

2. What is an equation for the translation of $y = -\dfrac{4.5}{x}$ that has asymptotes at $x = 3$ and $y = -5$?

   F. $y = -\dfrac{4.5}{x - 3} - 5$ **H.** $y = -\dfrac{4.5}{x - 5} + 3$

   G. $y = -\dfrac{4.5}{x + 3} - 5$ **J.** $y = -\dfrac{4.5}{x + 5} + 3$

3. Which is the graph of $y = \dfrac{1}{x + 1} - 2$?

   A. 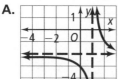   **B.** 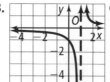   **C.** 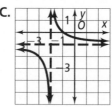   **D.**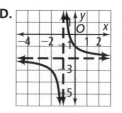

Extended Response

4. A race pilot's average rate of speed over a 720-mi course is inversely proportional to the time in minutes t the pilot takes to fly a complete race course. The pilot's final score s is the average speed minus any penalty points p earned.

   a. Write a function to model the pilot's score for a given t and p. (*Hint: $d = rt$*)

   b. Graph the function for a pilot who has 2 penalty points.

   c. What is the maximum time a pilot with 2 penalty points can take to finish the course and still earn a score of at least 3?

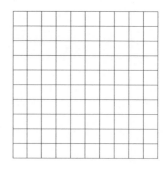

SOLVE IT!

Last season, you made 40% of your basketball shots. The Game 1 shot chart shows that you did not start this season so well. Starting with Game 2, how many consecutive shots must you make to raise this season's percentage to 40%? If you never miss another shot this season, how high can you raise your percentage? Explain your reasoning.

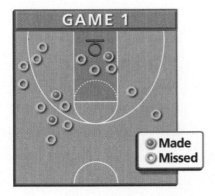

Interactive Exploration

Vocabulary Online

 Apply Mathematics (1)(A) Describe another real-world situation for which you could apply the same mathematical model.

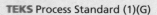

TEKS Process Standard (1)(G)

 Problem 1 | **Got It?** | **Finding Points of Discontinuity**

Learning
Animation

What are the domain and points of discontinuity of the rational function? Are the points of discontinuity *removable* or *non-removable*? What are the *x*- and *y*-intercepts of the rational function?

a. $y = \dfrac{1}{x^2 - 16}$

b. $y = \dfrac{x^2 - 1}{x^2 + 3}$

c. $y = \dfrac{x + 1}{x^2 + 3x + 2}$

ELPS Take notes as you listen to the solution for part (a). What steps are needed when finding points of discontinuity? How can you tell whether a discontinuity is removable? Use your notes to help you solve parts (b) and (c).

Problem 2 | Got It? | Finding Vertical Asymptotes

What are the vertical asymptotes for the graph of the rational function? What is the domain of each function? How do the vertical asymptotes relate to the domain?

Learning Animation

a. $y = \dfrac{x-2}{(x-1)(x+3)}$

b. $y = \dfrac{x-2}{(x-2)(x+3)}$

c. $y = \dfrac{x^2-1}{x+1}$

Problem 3 | Got It? | Finding Horizontal Asymptotes

What is the horizontal asymptote for the rational function?

Learning Animation

a. $y = \dfrac{-2x+6}{x-5}$

b. $y = \dfrac{x-1}{x^2+4x+4}$

c. $y = \dfrac{x^2+2x-3}{x-2}$

TEKS Process Standard (1)(D)

 Problem 4 | **Got It?** | **Graphing a Rational Function**

What is the graph of the rational function $y = \dfrac{x + 3}{x^2 - 6x + 5}$?

Learning
Animation

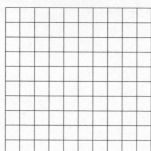

Problem 5 | **Got It?** | Using a Rational Function

Learning
Animation

a. You want to mix a 10% orange juice drink with 100% pure orange juice to make a 40% orange juice drink. The function $y = \dfrac{(2)(1.0) + x(0.1)}{2 + x}$ gives the concentration y of orange juice in the drink after you add x gallons of the 10% drink to 2 gallons of pure juice. How much of the 10% drink must you add to get a drink that is 40% juice?

b. If you want a drink that is 80% orange juice, would you need to add half as much of the 10% drink as your answer in part (a)? Explain.

Lesson Check

Do you know HOW?

1. Sketch the graph of $y = \dfrac{3x}{x-4}$.

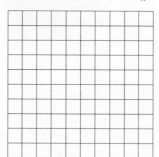

Math Tools

Online Practice

Virtual Nerd Tutorials

2. Write the equation of a rational function with a horizontal asymptote of $y = 2$ and a vertical asymptote of $x = -3$.

3. Issues of a magazine can be printed for $.42 each. The design cost is $80,000. 1200 copies of the magazine will be used as promotional copies and not sold. Write a function for the cost per magazine issue that is not a promotional copy. Identify the domain and range of your function using interval notation.

Do you UNDERSTAND?

Math
Tools

Online
Practice

Virtual Nerd
Tutorials

4. Vocabulary Identify any points of discontinuity for the rational function
$y = \dfrac{x^2 - 2x - 15}{x^2 - 6x + 5}$ and classify them as *removable* or *non-removable*.

5. Use Representations to Communicate Mathematical Ideas (1)(E)
Your friend claims that every rational function produces a graph with
vertical asymptotes. Write the equation of a counterexample to his
claim and sketch its graph.

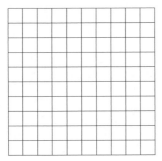

6. Evaluate Reasonableness (1)(B) What is the lowest possible degree of the
denominator of a rational function with vertical asymptotes at $y = -4$ and
$y = 4$? Explain how you know.

TEXAS Test Practice

Multiple Choice

For Exercises 1–4, choose the correct letter.

1. You want to make a sodium carbonate solution with a concentration of 2.5%. You have 50 mL of a 1% solution. About how many milliliters of a 6% solution should you add?

   A. 21   **B.** 26   **C.** 31   **D.** 36

2. What function has a graph with a removable discontinuity at $\left(5, \frac{1}{9}\right)$?

   F. $y = \dfrac{(x-5)}{(x+4)(x-5)}$ **H.** $y = \dfrac{4x-1}{5x+1}$

   G. $y = \dfrac{4}{x-5}$ **J.** $y = \dfrac{x+1}{5x-4}$

3. What best describes the horizontal asymptote(s), if any, of the graph of $y = \dfrac{x^2 + 2x - 8}{(x+6)^2}$?

   A. $y = -6$

   B. $y = 0$

   C. $y = 1$

   D. The graph has no horizontal asymptote.

4. Which rational function has a graph that has vertical asymptotes at $x = a$ and $x = -a$, and a horizontal asymptote at $y = 0$?

   F. $y = \dfrac{(x-a)(x+a)}{x}$ **H.** $y = \dfrac{x^2}{x^2 - a^2}$

   G. $y = \dfrac{1}{x^2 - a^2}$ **J.** $y = \dfrac{x-a}{x+a}$

Short Response

5. How many milliliters of 0.30% sugar solution must you add to 75 mL of a 4% sugar solution to get a 0.50% sugar solution? Show your work.

SOLVE IT!

The large rectangle and the small (non-square) rectangle are similar, so the ratios $\frac{\text{length}}{\text{width}}$ are equal. Explain why $x = 1 + \frac{1}{x}$. Explain how you can substitute for x on the right side (only) of the equation $x = 1 + \frac{1}{x}$, to get $x =$ an expression with no x.

Interactive Exploration

Vocabulary Online

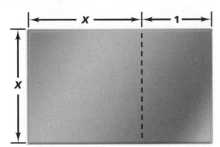

 Use Representations to Communicate Mathematical Ideas (1)(E)
Describe how the representation you used to solve the problem successfully organizes and communicates your ideas.

Problem 1 **Got It?** **Simplifying a Rational Expression**

What is the rational expression in simplest form? State any restrictions on the variables.

a. $\dfrac{24x^3y^2}{-6x^2y^3}$ **b.** $\dfrac{x^2 + 2x - 8}{x^2 - 5x + 6}$ **c.** $\dfrac{12 - 4x}{x^2 - 9}$

Learning Animation

 Problem 2 **Got It?** **Multiplying Rational Expressions**

What is the product $\dfrac{2x - 8}{x^2 - 16} \cdot \dfrac{x^2 + 5x + 4}{x^2 + 8x + 16}$ in simplest form? State any restrictions on the variable.

Learning Animation

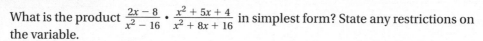

Problem 3 **Got It?** **Rewriting Quotients of Rational Expressions**

What is the quotient $\dfrac{x^2}{x^2 - 36} \div \dfrac{x^2}{x^2 + 16}$ in simplest form? State any restrictions on the variable.

Learning Animation

Lesson 11-4 │ **Rational Expressions**

416

Problem 4 | **Got It?** | **Dividing Rational Expressions**

a. What is the quotient $\frac{x^2 + 5x + 4}{x^2 + x - 12} \div \frac{x^2 - 1}{2x^2 - 6x}$ in simplest form? State any restrictions on the variable.

Learning Animation

b. Without doing the calculation, what is greatest number of restrictions the quotient $\frac{x^2 + 8x + 7}{x^2 - x - 12} \div \frac{x^2 + 2x - 8}{x^2 + 13x + 24}$ could have? Explain.

TEKS Process Standard (1)(A)

  Problem 5 | **Got It?** | **Using Rational Expressions to Solve a Problem**

Which shape of play space provides for a more efficient use of fencing, a square or an equilateral triangle? (*Hint:* The area of an equilateral triangle in terms of one side is $\frac{1}{2}(s)\left(\frac{\sqrt{3}}{2}s\right)$. The perimeter of an equilateral triangle is $3s$.)

Learning Animation

 Discuss a plan for solving the Got It with a classmate. Ask each other questions such as: How is the efficient use of fencing calculated? Do you always need to eliminate one of the variables in the ratios? Why does a greater ratio mean more efficient use?

Lesson Check

Do you know HOW?

1. Find the product and state any restrictions on the variable.

$$\frac{x^2 + 3x - 10}{x^2 + 4x - 12} \cdot \frac{3x + 18}{x + 3}$$

Math Tools

Online Practice

Virtual Nerd Tutorials

2. The product of a rational expression and $\frac{x^2 - 5x + 6}{x^2 + 4x + 3}$ is $\frac{x^2 - 4x + 4}{x^2 + x}$. What could the rational expression be? List any restrictions on x.

3. The area of a triangle is equal to one-half the product of the base and height. Write an expression in simplest form for the area of the triangle shown. Assume $x > 9$. List any other restrictions on x.

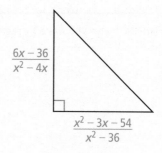

$\frac{6x - 36}{x^2 - 4x}$

$\frac{x^2 - 3x - 54}{x^2 - 36}$

Lesson Check

Do you UNDERSTAND?

Math
Tools

Online
Practice

Virtual Nerd
Tutorials

4. Vocabulary Is the equation $y = \frac{x+1}{x^2+1}$ in simplest form? Explain how you can tell.

5. Justify Mathematical Arguments (1)(G) A student claims that $x = 2$ is the only solution of the equation $\frac{x}{x-2} = \frac{2}{x-2}$. Is the student correct? Explain.

6. Connect Mathematical Ideas (1)(F) The area of a rectangle is represented by the expression $\frac{2a+20}{3a+15}$. The width of the rectangle is $\frac{a+10}{3a+24}$. Write an expression for the length of the rectangle in simplest form. Include any restrictions on a.

$$\frac{2a+20}{3a+15} \quad w$$

ℓ

TEXAS Test Practice

Multiple Choice

For Exercises 1–4, choose the correct letter.

1. What is the area of the triangle shown at the right?

   A. $\dfrac{2x+8}{x^2-6x+9}$ **C.** $\dfrac{x+4}{x^2-6x+9}$

   B. $\dfrac{x^2+6x+9}{x+4}$ **D.** $\dfrac{2x^2+12x+18}{x+4}$

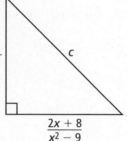

2. Which of the following statements is true for
$f(x)=\dfrac{x-2}{1-x}\cdot\dfrac{1}{x-2}$ and $g(x)=\dfrac{1}{1-x}$?

   F. $f(x)$ and $g(x)$ have the same domain.

   G. $x=-1$ is not in the domain of either $f(x)$ or $g(x)$.

   H. $x=2$ and $x=1$ are not in the domain of $g(x)$.

   J. $x=2$ is not in the domain of $f(x)$.

3. Which expression equals $\dfrac{t^2-1}{t-2}\cdot\dfrac{t^2-3t+2}{t^2+4t+3}$?

   A. $\dfrac{t^2-2t+1}{t+3}$ **C.** $\dfrac{(t+1)^2(t+3)}{(t-2)^2}$

   B. $\dfrac{t^2-1}{t+3}$ **D.** $\dfrac{2t^2-3t+1}{t^2+5t+1}$

4. Which expression equals $\dfrac{x^2-4x-5}{x^2+6x+5}$?

   F. $x+1$ **H.** $\dfrac{x-5}{x+5}$

   G. $-10x-10$ **J.** $\dfrac{4x-5}{6x+5}$

Short Response

5. What is the quotient $\dfrac{y+2}{2y^2-3y-2}\div\dfrac{y^2-4}{y^2+y-6}$ expressed in simplest form? State any restrictions on the variable. Show your work.

SOLVE IT!

At 3 P.M., four runners all leave the starting line, running laps around the indoor track. If the runners maintain their pace, at what time will Sue, Drew, and Stu finish a lap together? At what time will all four runners finish a lap together? Explain your reasoning.

Lap Time	
Name	**Time**
Sue	1:30
Drew	2:00
Stu	1:12
Marylou	1:20

Interactive Exploration

Vocabulary Online

 Analyze Mathematical Relationships (1)(F) What mathematical relationships did you identify in the problem? How did you use them to solve the problem?

Problem 1 | **Got It?** | Finding the Least Common Multiple

What is the LCM of the expressions?

a. $2x + 4$ and $x^2 - x - 6$

b. $x^2 + 3x - 4$, $x^2 + 2x - 8$, and $x^2 - 4x + 4$

Learning
Animation

 Problem 2 | **Got It?** | Finding the Least Common Denominator

Find the LCD of $\frac{x-2}{x^2-x}$ and $\frac{3}{x^2-1}$.

Learning
Animation

Lesson 11-5 | Adding and Subtracting Rational Expressions

422

Problem 3 **Got It?** Adding Rational Expressions

What is the sum of the two rational expressions in simplest form? State any restrictions on the variable.

a. $\dfrac{x+1}{x-1} + \dfrac{-2}{x^2-x}$

b. $\dfrac{x}{x^2-4} + \dfrac{1}{x+2}$

c. Is it possible to add the rational expressions in Problem 3 by finding a common denominator, but not the *least* common denominator? Explain.

Problem 4 **Got It?** Subtracting Rational Expressions

What is the difference of the two rational expressions in simplest form? State any restrictions on the variable.

a. $\dfrac{x+3}{x-2} - \dfrac{6x-7}{x^2-3x+2}$

b. $\dfrac{x-1}{x+5} - \dfrac{x+3}{x^2+6x+5}$

Lesson 11-5 | Adding and Subtracting Rational Expressions

423

Problem 5 **Got It?** **Simplifying a Complex Fraction**

What is a simpler form of the complex fraction? State any restrictions on the variables.

Learning
Animation

a. $\dfrac{x}{\frac{1}{x} + \frac{1}{y}}$

b. $\dfrac{\frac{x-2}{x} + \frac{2}{x+1}}{\frac{3}{x-1} - \frac{1}{x+1}}$

ELPS Discuss with a partner the process of simplifying complex fractions. Work together to write two questions to ask your teacher that will help you understand this process. Once your questions are answered, identify the method you prefer to use and explain your reasoning.

Problem 6 | **Got It?** | **Using Rational Expressions to Solve a Problem**

Learning
Animation

A woman drives an SUV that gets 10 mi/gal (mpg). Her husband drives a hybrid that gets 60 mpg. Every week, they travel the same number of miles. They want to improve their combined mpg. In Problem 5, you found that Option 1 gave a better combined mpg than Option 2.

Suppose they consider a third option, shown below.

Option 1: They can tune the SUV and increase its mileage by 1 mpg and keep the hybrid as it is.

Option 2: They can buy a new hybrid that gets 80 mpg and keep the SUV as it is.

Option 3: They can replace the hybrid with a new hybrid that will get double the mileage of the present hybrid and keep the SUV as it is.

Which of the three options will give them the best combined mpg?

Math Tools

Online Practice

Virtual Nerd Tutorials

Lesson Check

Do you know **HOW?**

1. Simplify. State any restrictions on the variable.

$$\frac{b-4}{b^2+2b-8} - \frac{b+2}{b^2-16}$$

2. The profit, in dollars, made on each pizza sold by a local restaurant is modeled by the expression $2 + \frac{x}{4x-20}$, where x is the number of minutes spent making the pizza. Simplify the expression. Use your model to determine the profit made on a pizza that took 20 minutes to prepare.

3. Write two rational expressions whose sum is $\frac{6x-11}{x^2-4}$ for $x \neq 2$ and $x \neq -2$.

Lesson Check

Do you UNDERSTAND?

Math Tools

Online Practice

Virtual Nerd Tutorials

4. Vocabulary Explain how any complex fraction can be rewritten in a simpler form.

5. Use a Problem-Solving Model (1)(B) Describe and correct the error made in simplifying the complex fraction.

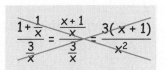

6. Connect Mathematical Ideas (1)(F) Write two rational expressions that simplify to $\frac{x+1}{x-5}$.

Multiple Choice

For Exercises 1–4, choose the correct letter.

1. The harmonic mean of two numbers a and b equals $\dfrac{2}{\frac{1}{a} + \frac{1}{b}}$. Which expression equals the harmonic mean of x and $x + 1$?

   A. $\dfrac{2}{x^2 + x}$

   B. $\dfrac{4x + 2}{x^2 + x}$

   C. $2x + 1$

   D. $\dfrac{2x^2 + 2x}{2x + 1}$

2. Which expression equals $\dfrac{\frac{2}{m} + 6}{\frac{1}{n}}$?

   F. $\dfrac{12n}{m}$

   G. $\dfrac{2n + 6mn}{m}$

   H. $\dfrac{6m + 2}{mn}$

   J. $\dfrac{m}{2n + 6mn}$

3. Which is the least common denominator of fractions that have denominators $5x + 10$ and $25x^2 - 100$?

   A. $5(x - 2)$

   B. $5(x^2 - 20)$

   C. $25(x^2 - 4)$

   D. $75(x + 2)(x^2 - 4)$

4. If p and q are prime numbers, then which of the following is true about $\dfrac{1}{px} - \dfrac{1}{qx}$ when written in simplified form?

   F. The denominator will always be divisible by pq.

   G. The denominator will always be divisible by x^2.

   H. The denominator will be divisible by p or by q, but not by both.

   J. The denominator will not be divisible by either p or q.

Short Response

5. Subtract $3 - \dfrac{1}{x^2 + 5}$. Write your answer in simplest form. State any restrictions on the variable. Show your work.

 **SOLVE IT!**

Scan page for an interactive version of this Solve It.

You normally walk the sidewalk from home to school in 25 minutes. If you walked the shortcut at your normal constant rate, how much time would you save?

If you jog to school at a constant rate, you save 4 minutes by jogging the shortcut. How long does it take you to jog the sidewalk to school?

Interactive Exploration

Vocabulary Online

School

Home

 Connect Mathematical Ideas (1)(F) What prior knowledge did you draw on to solve the problem?

TEKS Process Standard (1)(C)

 Problem 1 | **Got It?** | **Solving a Rational Equation**

Solve each rational equation. Check each solution for reasonableness.

Learning
Animation

a. $\dfrac{x-1}{x+2} = \dfrac{x^2 + 2x - 3}{x+2}$

b. $\dfrac{x}{x+1} + \dfrac{3}{x+4} = \dfrac{x+3}{x+4}$

Problem 2 | **Got It?** | **Using Rational Equations**

 Learning Animation

When you ride your bike in the direction of the wind, the wind's speed is added to your riding speed. When you ride against the wind, the wind's speed is subtracted from your riding speed.

a. You ride your bike to a store 4 mi away to pick up things for dinner. When there is no wind, you ride at 10 mi/h. Today your trip to the store and back took 1 hour. Write a rational equation you can use to find the speed of the wind today.

b. Solve the equation you wrote in part (a). Discuss which solution is reasonable in the context of the situation.

c. Explain why there is no difference between the travel time to and from the store when there is no wind.

ELPS Discuss part (a) with a classmate. What pronoun indicates that part (a) is written from the second person point of view? What pronouns can you use to rewrite part (a) in the first person point of view? What about the third person point of view?

 Problem 3 | **Got It?** | **Using a Graphing Calculator to Solve a Rational Equation**

 Learning Animation

What are the solutions of the rational equation $\frac{x+2}{1-2x} = 5$? Use a graphing calculator to solve.

Lesson Check

Do you know HOW?

1. Solve the equation. Check each solution.

$$\frac{2}{n} + \frac{n+2}{n+1} = \frac{-2}{n^2+n}$$

2. Solve the equation. Check each solution.

$$\frac{x+1}{x-2} = \frac{3x+6}{x^2-4}$$

3. One pump can fill a tank with oil in 4 hours. A second pump can fill the same tank in 3 hours. If both pumps are used at the same time, how long will they take to fill the tank?

Math Tools

Online Practice

Virtual Nerd Tutorials

Lesson Check

Do you UNDERSTAND?

4. **Select Techniques to Solve Problems (1)(C)** Describe two methods you can use to check whether a solution is extraneous.

Math Tools

Online Practice

Virtual Nerd Tutorials

5. **Use a Problem-Solving Model (1)(B)** Describe and correct the error made in solving the equation.

$$\frac{5}{x} + \frac{9}{7} = \frac{28}{x}$$

$$\frac{14}{x+7} = \frac{28}{x}$$

$$14x = 28(x+7)$$

$$14x = 28x + 196$$

$$-196 = 14x$$

$$-14 = x$$

6. **Select Tools to Solve Problems (1)(C)** Describe two ways to use technology to find the solutions of $\frac{3}{x-5} = \frac{2}{x^2-4x-5}$.

Gridded Response

Enter your answer in the grid provided.

1. Your biology class has five tests over the course of the semester, and your score on the first one is 78. If you score 95 on every test for the rest of the semester, how many more tests would it take to raise your average for the class above 90?

For Exercises 2–4, what is the solution of the rational equation?

2. $\dfrac{2}{6x+2} = \dfrac{x}{3x^2+11}$

3. $\dfrac{3}{2x-4} = \dfrac{5}{3x+7}$

4. $\dfrac{2}{x+2} + \dfrac{5}{x-2} = \dfrac{6}{x^2-4}$

1. 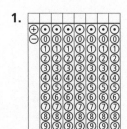 **2.** 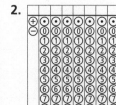 **3.** 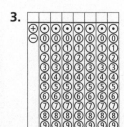 **4.**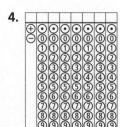

Lesson 11-6 │ **Solving Rational Equations**

434

SOLVE IT!

How many small triangles will be in Stage 9? Explain your reasoning.

Stage 1   **Stage 2**   **Stage 3**   **Stage 4**

Interactive Exploration

Vocabulary Online

Use Multiple Representations to Communicate Mathematical Ideas (1)(D)
What is another representation you could use to present your solution? Explain how the representation communicates the same information.

TEKS Process Standard (1)(F)

 Problem 1 | **Got It?** | Analyzing Data to Choose a Model

Use the scatter plot. Which of the following equations would be most appropriate to use as an exponential model for the data? Explain.

(I) $y = -431(0.78)^x - 2.6$
(II) $y = 0.12(1.28)^x + 431$
(III) $y = 431(0.78)^x$

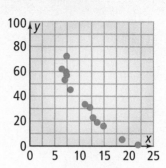

Learning Animation

TEKS Process Standard (1)(D)

 Problem 2 | **Got It?** | Choosing a Model Using Differences or Ratios

Which type of function best models the ordered pairs $(-1, 0.5)$, $(0, 1)$, $(1, 2)$, $(2, 4)$, and $(3, 8)$? Use differences or ratios.

ELPS Share information to solve the Got It together. What operation do you use to test for a common difference? What about a common ratio? Which coordinates do you use to test for a common difference or common ratio? Is the problem easier if you first set up a table?

Problem 3 | **Got It?** | Modeling Real-World Data

Learning
Animation

The table shows the annual income of a tech company in millions of dollars.
Which type of function best models the data? Write an equation to model the data.

Tech Company Annual Income					
Year	0	1	2	3	4
Income (millions of $)	18.3	18.7	19.2	19.7	20.2

Do you know HOW?

1. Which type of function best models the data in the table? Write an equation to model the data.

x	y
0	102.2
1	153.3
2	230.0
3	345.0
4	517.5

Math Tools

Online Practice

Virtual Nerd Tutorials

2. The data in the table are best modeled by a quadratic function. What are the missing y-values in the table?

x	y
4	9
5	17
6	29
7	
8	

3. The table shows the length y of a cave formation at various times x after scientists start measuring it. The x-values in the table do not have a common difference. Is it still possible to determine which type of function best models the data? If so, explain why and write an equation to model the data. If not, explain why not.

Length of Cave Formation

Time (yr)	Length (mm)
5	105.65
15	106.95
22	107.86
28	108.58
42	110.46

Lesson Check

Do you UNDERSTAND?

4. **Explain Mathematical Ideas (1)(G)** Explain how to use common differences and common ratios to decide which type of function is the most appropriate model for a set of data.

Math Tools

Online Practice

Virtual Nerd Tutorials

5. **Evaluate Reasonableness (1)(B)** A classmate examined the table of data below and stated that a linear function perfectly models the data since the y-values have a common difference of 2. Do you agree? Explain.

x	y
1	4
2	6
4	8
8	10
16	12

6. **Justify Mathematical Arguments (1)(G)** If the y-values in a set of data pairs have a common difference not equal to zero, can they also have a common ratio? Explain why or why not.

TEXAS Test Practice

Multiple Choice

For Exercises 1–4, choose the correct letter.

1. The attendance at the high school basketball games seems to be affected by the success of the team. The graph at the right models the attendance over the first half of the season. Which function would also represent the data shown in the graph, where a represents the attendance and g represents the number of games the team has won?

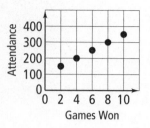

   A. $a = 25(3)^g$ **C.** $a = 25g^2 + 100$

   B. $a = 25g + 100$ **D.** $a = -25g^2 + 100$

2. Which kind of function best models the set of data points $(-3, 18)$, $(-2, 6)$, $(-1, 2)$, $(0, 11)$, $(1, 27)$?

   F. linear   **H.** exponential

   G. quadratic   **J.** none of the above

3. Which kind of function can be used to model data pairs that have a common ratio?

   A. linear   **C.** exponential

   B. quadratic   **D.** none of the above

4. A teacher is buying paintbrushes for students in an art class. She would pay $0.50 for one paintbrush, $1.00 for two, $1.50 for three, and $2.00 for four. Which kind of function can be used to model the total cost paid for the paintbrushes bought by the teacher?

   F. linear   **H.** exponential

   G. quadratic   **J.** none of the above

Short Response

5. The data in the table show the population growth of a city since the year 2000. What kind of function models the data? How do you know?

Year	Population
0	5275
1	10,550
2	21,100
3	42,200
4	84,400

SOLVE IT!

The graph shows the number of hours you worked and the amount of money you earned each day last week. How many hours should you work to earn $200? What assumptions did you make to find your answer? Explain.

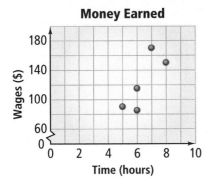

Interactive Exploration

Vocabulary Online

 Evaluate Reasonableness (1)(B) Explain how you know your solution is reasonable.

TEKS Process Standard (1)(A)

 Problem 1 | **Got It?** | **Finding the Line of Best Fit**

Learning Animation

The table lists the cost of 2% milk. Use a scatter plot to find the equation of the line of best fit. Use your model to predict the cost of one gallon of 2% milk in 2025.

Cost of 2% Milk						
Year	1998	2000	2002	2004	2006	2008
Average cost for one gallon ($)	2.57	2.83	2.93	2.93	3.10	3.71

SOURCE: U.S. Department of Agriculture

ELPS Use routine language to explain the instructions in your own words. Which word in the instructions hints that you will make a prediction? What will you be predicting? What kind of model does the Got It say you should use to make your prediction?

Problem 2 | **Got It?** | Using Exponential Regression to Make Predictions

Learning Animation

a. Use the exponential model $y = 116(0.967)^x + 40$ from Problem 2, where x is the number of minutes and y is the temperature, in °F. Predict how long it will take for the soup to reach a temperature of 42°F.

b. In Problem 2, would the model of the exponential data be useful if you did not translate the data by 40 units? Explain.

TEKS Process Standard (1)(F)

Problem 3 | **Got It?** | Select the Best Model and Make Predictions

Learning Animation

The table shows the history of temperatures for a summer day in San Antonio, Texas. What is a quadratic model for these data? Predict the high temperature for the day. At what time does the high temperature occur?

San Antonio, TX

Time	Predicted Temperature (°F)
6 A.M.	68
9 A.M.	81
12 P.M.	91
3 P.M.	94
6 P.M.	90
9 P.M.	81

Lesson Check

Do you know HOW?

1. The table below shows the cost of a taxi ride for trips of various distances. Use a calculator to find the equation for the line of best fit. Then use the model to predict the cost of a 20-mile taxi ride.

Taxi Fares						
Distance (mi)	3	5	7	9	11	13
Fare ($)	9.60	14.20	18.55	23.50	27.95	32.55

Math Tools

Online Practice

Virtual Nerd Tutorials

2. For which of the three values of n below are the data in the table best modeled using exponential regression? Find the exponential model.

   A. 210

   B. 217

   C. 227

x	y
3	150
4	180
5	n

3. The table shows the price of a stock at various numbers of months after it was first offered to the public. Using the model that is most appropriate for the data, predict the amount of increase or decrease in the price of the stock from Month 8 to Month 9.

Stock Prices						
Months	1	2	3	4	5	6
Price ($)	52.50	48.10	44.60	42.20	40.50	40.00

Lesson Check

Do you UNDERSTAND?

Math Tools

Online Practice

Virtual Nerd Tutorials

4. **Vocabulary** How are exponential and quadratic regression similar? How are they different?

5. **Explain Mathematical Ideas (1)(G)** Your classmate says that since two data points are enough to define a line of best fit using the LinReg feature on your calculator, it makes sense to use linear regression to model these data. Do you agree? Why or why not?

Year	Population
2010	6,200
2012	6,300

6. **Evaluate Reasonableness (1)(B)** A student used linear regression to model the data at the right with the equation $y = 0.05x + 7.95$. Without using a calculator, state whether the student's model is reasonable. Explain your answer.

x	y
1	7.89
4	7.72
7	7.54
10	7.39
13	7.22

Lesson 12-2 │ Using Regression to Choose a Model and Make Predictions

TEXAS Test Practice

Multiple Choice

For Exercises 1–4, choose the correct letter.

1. The table shows the average price of a home in a nearby town for several years since 2000. Using an exponential model, which of the following is the best prediction of the average price of a home in the town in 2018?

   A. $253,000
   C. $277,000
   B. $264,000
   D. $288,000

   Home Prices

Year	Average Price ($)
2000	$130,000
2004	$156,000
2008	$187,000
2012	$220,000

2. Which of the following types of models is the best fit for the data in the table at the right?

   F. linear with positive slope
   H. quadratic
   G. linear with negative slope
   J. exponential

x	y
3	11.8
4	10.8
5	10.2
6	10.6

3. Which set of ordered pairs is best modeled using exponential regression?

   A. $(2, 4.1)$, $(3, 5.8)$, $(4, 7.6)$, and $(5, 9.1)$

   B. $(6, 1.5)$, $(7, 3.1)$, $(8, 5.5)$, and $(9, 8.9)$

   C. $(1, 2.5)$, $(2, 4.5)$, $(3, 8.1)$, and $(4, 14.6)$

   D. $(5, 9.2)$, $(6, 7.8)$, $(7, 6.3)$, and $(8, 4.9)$

4. The y-values of a data set increase and then decrease as the x-values increase. Which of the following models is most likely to fit the data?

   F. $y = 0.35x^2 - 4.56x - 1.02$
   H. $y = 1.41(0.96)^x + 5.12$
   G. $y = -1.25x^2 + 3.88x + 2.51$
   J. $y = -3.05x + 4.61$

Short Response

5. The table shows the profit that a printing company makes when they print different numbers of posters.

Poster Profits						
Number of Posters	150	200	250	300	350	400
Profit ($)	55	110	175	250	350	460

   a. What type of model best fits the data?

   b. Use your calculator to write a function for the model and predict the profit from printing 600 posters.

SOLVE IT!

A shipping company wants to replace the brakes on its fleet of trucks with safer brakes. The table below shows speed and average stopping distances for two different brands of brakes (in good condition on a level, dry road). Which type of function best models each data set? What else do you need to know about the company in order to determine which brakes it should choose? Explain.

Interactive Exploration

Vocabulary Online

Speed (mi/h)	Average Stopping Distance (ft)	
	Brand A	Brand B
10	13	6
20	31	25
30	61	57
40	104	103
50	156	160
60	215	230

 Connect Mathematical Ideas (1)(F) How does this problem relate to a problem you have seen before?

Problem 1 | Got It? | Using Linear Models

The manager of a T-shirt shop has been testing various prices for T-shirts. She randomly selects a sample of days from the previous year and records the price and the number of T-shirts sold that day. The table shows her data.

a. What is a model for the data using regression?

Learning Animation

Price ($)	Daily Sales
9.99	81
10.99	69
9.99	72
6.99	124
12.99	68
14.99	49
8.50	93
9.99	69
12.99	56
9.99	75

b. The store plans to hold a two-day sale selling T-shirts for $8.99. The store pays $4.73 per T-shirt. Estimate the store's profit during the sale.

ELPS Take turns listening and speaking about *regression analysis* and *linear models*. Listen carefully as your classmate speaks. Continue to alternate roles for three rounds. Are you able to explain concepts with more detail by the third round?

Problem 2 **Got It?** **Using Quadratic Models**

The health department for a major city recorded data during an epidemic of an infectious disease. The table shows the number of new cases reported per 100,000 people for select days. Day 0 is the first day any cases were reported.

a. What is a model for the data using regression?

b. The health department considers the epidemic over on the first day that the number of new cases reported is less than one tenth of the maximum number. Make a judgment based on the model in part (a) to decide on which day the health department would consider this epidemic over. Explain your reasoning.

Day	Number of New Cases (per 100,000)
0	2
3	3
18	31
28	55
36	87
45	98
53	107
59	92
67	80
71	63
85	46
92	16
101	12
110	9

Learning Animation

Lesson 12-3 | **Using Models to Make Decisions and Judgments**

449

TEKS Process Standard (1)(F)

 Problem 3 | **Got It?** | **Using Exponential Models**

The population of a city for various years since 1975 is shown in the table.

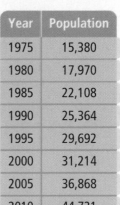

Learning Animation

Year	Population
1975	15,380
1980	17,970
1985	22,108
1990	25,364
1995	29,692
2000	31,214
2005	36,868
2010	44,721

a. Use regression to find a model for the data, using years since 1970 as your *x*-values.

b. City engineers have determined that the city's sewer system can handle a population of up to 60,000 people. It will take 3 years to plan and build an expansion of the sewer system. Make a judgment based on the model in part (a) to decide in what year the city should begin to plan an expansion?

Problem 4 | **Got It?** | **Using an Experiment to Model Nuclear Decay**

Learning
Animation

Using the model from part B of Problem 4, when is there 26.5 grams of the parent atoms?

Lessen Check

Do you know HOW?

1. The table shows the average retail price of one dozen eggs in various years since 1981. A family buys one dozen eggs each week. What is a model for the data using regression? In what year will the family first spend more than $100 on eggs?

Year	Price ($)
1981	0.90
1986	0.87
1991	0.99
1996	1.11
2001	0.93
2006	1.31
2010	1.66
2011	1.73

Math Tools

Online Practice

Virtual Nerd Tutorials

2. A city has a birth rate of 12.75, which means the average annual number of births per 1000 residents is 12.75. The table shows the population of the city in various years since 1995. Hospital administrators are planning a new maternity wing for the year 2020. What is a model for the data using regression? How many births will occur in the city in 2020? Round to the nearest thousand.

Year	Population (millions)
1995	1.38
1997	1.44
2000	1.52
2002	1.59
2005	1.68
2007	1.75
2010	1.86
2013	1.97

3. The table shows the annual revenues and annual costs in various years for a freelance designer. Based on the most appropriate models for the revenue data and for the cost data, in what year will the designer make the greatest profit? (*Hint:* profit = revenues − costs)

Annual Revenues and Costs

Year	Revenues ($)	Costs ($)
2000	17,200	18,900
2004	41,200	12,900
2007	55,500	9,500
2010	65,200	6,950
2012	70,100	5,750

Lesson Check

Do you UNDERSTAND?

Math Tools

Online Practice

Virtual Nerd Tutorials

4. **Vocabulary** Which of the three regression models from this lesson may have a minimum or maximum value? Explain.

5. **Explain Mathematical Ideas (1)(G)** A student uses regression to find a linear model that represents the total cost $f(x)$ of manufacturing x portable music players. Explain how the student can modify the model to write a function that represents the unit cost c of manufacturing a single portable music player when a total of x players are produced.

6. **Evaluate Reasonableness (1)(B)** A student used the table of population data from Exercise 2 and exponential regression to predict that there will be about 52,000 births in the city in 2050. Is this likely to be a reasonable prediction? Why or why not?

TEXAS Test Practice

Multiple Choice

For Exercises 1–4, choose the correct letter.

1. The table shows the total cost of ordering different numbers of custom T-shirts. Based on a linear model, which of the following is the best estimate of the average cost per shirt when you order 50 shirts?

   A. $6.53

   B. $7.94

   C. $13.49

   D. $16.43

   Custom T-Shirts

Number of Shirts	Total Cost ($)
8	63.50
15	107.30
19	132.50
28	188.60

2. You use exponential regression to model the number of subscribers $f(x)$ to an online file-sharing service x years after 2000. Assuming each subscriber pays $23 per year, which expression can you use to find the increase in revenues from subscribers from 2015 to 2016?

   F. $23f(16) - f(15)$

   G. $23[f(16) - f(15)]$

   H. $23[f(15) - f(16)]$

   J. $23[f(16) + f(15)]$

3. Based on linear regression, the equation $y = 3.75x + 61$ models the total cost y to have a carpet installed, where x is the carpet's area in square feet. Which of the following is the minimum area of carpeting you can have installed so that the cost is less than $5 per square foot?

   A. 16 ft^2 **B.** 28 ft^2 **C.** 49 ft^2 **D.** 80 ft^2

4. You are given a randomly selected set of data showing admission prices to an aquarium and the number of daily visitors at each price. You use linear regression to model the number of visitors $f(x)$ at a price of x dollars. How can you estimate the price at which the total daily revenue from visitors is $20,000?

   F. Evaluate $f(20,000)$.

   G. Solve $f(x) = 20,000$.

   H. Find the intersection of the graphs of $y = \frac{f(x)}{x}$ and $y = 20,000$.

   J. Determine the value of x for which $xf(x) = 20,000$.

Extended Response

5. The table shows the populations of two towns in various years. What is a model for the population of each town using regression? Predict the year in which the two towns' populations will be equal.

Year	Population	
	Greely	Hylan
2000	42,320	95,010
2004	47,630	87,620
2009	55,220	79,200
2012	60,330	74,550

Lesson 12-3 | Using Models to Make Decisions and Judgments